WEB 2.0
Hot Apps
Cool Projects
SCIENCE
2nd Edition

Jim Holland and Susan Anderson

Standards

Aligned with the TEKS   iste

VISIONS™

TECHNOLOGY IN EDUCATION

PUBLISHER OF QUALITY EDUCATIONAL PRODUCTS

Production Coordinator
David Hoerger

Copy Editor
David Hoerger

Cover Design
Tim Yost

Visions Technology
P.O. Box 70479
Eugene, OR 97401

Phone: 541.349.0905
Fax: 541.349.0944
Email: info@teamvistech.com
Web site: www.toolsforteachers.com

ISBN: 978-1-58912-902-3

Table of Contents

Introduction to Web 2.0 Hot Apps/Cool Projects

Web 2.0 Disclaimers 1

Student Safety & Privacy 2

Student Email 2

Creating Accounts for Students 3

Copyright-friendly Image Sources 4

Similar/Alternate Web 2.0 Sites 9

Animoto

Animoto 11

User's Guide to Animoto 12

    Applying for an All-Access Teacher Account 12

    Creating Accounts for Students 12

    Student Registration Sheet 13

    Starting a New Video Project 14

    Uploading Images 15

    Adding Animoto Title Slides 16

    Creating a Custom Title Slide Using PowerPoint 17

    Editing Images 20

    Adding Music 23

    Finalizing the Video 25

    Viewing Videos 26

    Re-mixing a Video 26

    Sharing Videos 27

    Downloading the Video as an MP4 File 27

    Linking to the Video on the Animoto Website 27

    Embedding the Video into another Website 28

Storyboard for Animoto Videos 30

Big Huge Labs Trading Cards

Big Huge Labs 33

User's Guide to BigHugeLab's Trading Cards 34

   Creating a Teacher Account 34

   Creating Student Accounts 35

   Creating Trading Cards 36

TypeWithMe

TypeWithMe 41

User's Guide to TypeWithMe 42

   Creating a Pad 42

   Sharing Your Pad 42

   Before Editing 42

   Editing the Document 43

   Saving Versions of your Work 43

   Exporting your Final Draft 44

Mixbook

Mixbook 47

User's Guide to Mixbook 48

   Creating an Account 48

   Starting a New Mixbook 48

   Resume Editing a Mixbook 51

   Uploading Photos to My Photos 51

   Adding/Removing Pages 52

   Selecting the Background 53

   Editing the Background 54

   Selecting Layouts 55

Adding/Editing Photos & Stickers 55

Adding/Editing Text...57

Publishing the Book 59

Storyboard for Mixbooks 62

Scrapblog

Scrapblog 65

User's Guide to Scrapblog 66

Creating an account...66

Starting a new scrapblog 67

Getting video...68

Selecting backgrounds...69

Adding text boxes 70

Stickers, frames and shapes (Embellishments)............................72

Overlapping...73

Adding new slides 74

Deleting a page...74

Changing the order of the pages 74

Adding transitions 75

Adding music 75

Publishing 76

Editing an existing Scrapblog...77

TinyPaste

TinyPaste 79

User's Guide to TinyPaste..80

Creating a TinyPaste 80

Editing the TinyPaste 80

Adding a Link 81

Adding an image 82

Adding a video 82

Finishing the posting 83

Voki

Voki 85

User's Guide to Voki 86

Creating a Voki 86

Customize your character 87

Recording the voice 88

Selecting a background 89

Select a player 90

Publishing your Voki 90

Wordle

Wordle 93

User's Guide to Wordle 94

Creating a Wordle 94

Customizing the Wordle 95

Printing and Saving Wordles 96

Online Samples of Lessons

Animoto 98

Mixbook 98

Scrapblog 99

TinyPaste 99

Voki 99

General Science Projects

TypeWithMe: Scrambled Lab Report 101

TypeWithMe: Lab Safety Guidelines 107

TinyPaste: Tools of Science 111

BigHugeLabs Trading Cards: Metric Measurement 115

TypeWithMe: Famous Scientists 119

Scrapblog: Science Fair Project 123

Cell Biology Projects

TinyPaste: Cellular Organisms 131

TypeWithMe: Steps of Mitosis 135

Human Body

BigHugeLabs Trading Cards: Digestive Process 139

Wordle: Acquired and Inherited Traits 143

Mixbook: The Five Senses 147

Zoology and Botany

Animoto Video: Characteristics of Living Things 151

Wordle: Five Kingdoms 157

TinyPaste: Insects 161

Scrapblog: Butterfly Life Cycle 165

Voki: Dinosaur Mystery 171

Animoto Video: Food from Plant Parts 175

Voki: Photosynthesis 179

Ecology

Mixbook: Biomes 183

Scrapblog: Producers, Consumers & Decomposers 187

TinyPaste: Food Chain 191

BigHugeLabs Trading Cards: Animal Adaptations 195

Earth and Space

Wordle: Landforms 199

Voki: Forces of Nature 203

Mixbook: Rock Classification & Cycles 207

Voki: Characteristics of the Moon 211

Voki: Ocean Tides 215

BigHugeLabs Trading Cards: The Eight Planets 219

Energy and Motion

Scrapblog: States of Matter 223

Animoto Video: Energy Forms 229

Scrapblog: Electromagnetic Spectrum 233

Mixbook: Simple Machines 237

Chemistry

Mixbook: Common Uses of the Elements 241

Weather and Erosion

Wordle: 4 Seasons 245

Animoto Video: Water Cycle 249

Animoto Video: Natural Disasters 253

Web 2.0 Disclaimers

The convenience of using free, web-based tools does not come without some important stipulations. All educators should be aware of the following issues.

Definition
There are as many definitions of "Web 2.0" as there are users on the Internet. This book's tools and lessons will approach Web 2.0 according to this working definition:

> *Web 2.0 is the next generation of the Internet where the content of the web is created or edited by end-users (either individually or collaboratively) rather than those few geeky computer nerds. Further, these sites often allow collaboration, sharing, and assimilation to bring about exchanges of ideas from many different perspectives in the form of text, photos, videos, and/or other multimedia components.*

"Free" Sites
Web 2.0 sites change constantly – what may be free and simple today may not be on the day of your lesson. This includes the websites used in this book!

User Guides & Screenshots
Because of the ever-evolving nature of these Web 2.0 sites, the step-by-step instructions and screenshots used in this book may become outdated and irrelevant.

Reliable Network Connection
A reliable network connection is critical – most sites won't allow you to download your creation.

Blocked Sites
Sites that are not blocked/filtered out by your network today may be blocked tomorrow – always have a backup plan.

Inappropriate Content
Even though a website may be unblocked, inappropriate content often shows up in the user gallery and "just created" sections of some websites.

Tips & Tricks
* Many Web 2.0 sites take advantage of photo hosting sites – find one that works for you. (We use Flickr.com.)
* You won't remember all your logins and passwords – create a spreadsheet and password protect it.
* Be prepared to showcase widgets on your own blog, wiki, or website.

Student Safety & Privacy

Student safety and privacy must be considered at all times. Using Web 2.0 tools, students become instant web publishers. This can be dangerous!

Students are instantly publishing to a site beyond your control! We hope this scares you! Before beginning any Web 2.0 project, review your own policies and procedures about acceptable use and online safety. Some suggested procedures to discuss for safety reasons include:

- No chat rooms
- No use of real names (assign or select pseudonyms)
- No distribution of personal information of any kind
- No use of student pictures
- What to do if inappropriate material is encountered
- Consequences of violating the acceptable use policy

Student Email

Student email addresses may be necessary to create accounts at certain Web 2.0 websites (see login methods). While some districts provide student email accounts, many do not. If student email accounts become necessary, consider using either Gaggle.net or Epals.com (preferred).

- Only teachers can create accounts, not students.
- Teachers can access sent/received mail.
- Built-in filters flag inappropriate content and require teacher approval before sending/receiving.
- Teachers can suspend accounts.
- May include blogging and chat.

Consider this:
- Communicate with parents about the accounts (parent letters are available on the sites).
- Filtered email is not 100% successful – actively monitor.
- Students must be taught how to handle inappropriate content.
- The same privacy/safety rules above also apply to email.

Creating Accounts for Students

Most Web 2.0 sites require users to create accounts and log in to the site so their work can be stored and retrieved when needed. Many of these websites do not allow account holders to be under 13 years old, so read the fine print. If you don't want to hassle with student email accounts, consider using the following methods to log in to various sites:

Method #1: One Size Fits All
- All students use the same generic login created by the teacher.
- This won't work for most sites.
- Doing this allows students to change the account settings.
- Students may have access to delete/change the work of others.

Method #2: Fake It!
- Most registrations require an email address – this is usually used for the sole purpose of retrieving lost passwords or getting updates.
- Enter a fake email address!
- Understand that if a password is forgotten, the account is lost!

Method #3: Piggy-back It! (recommended)
- Teacher creates the main email address.
- Students "piggy-back" off that email address.
- Two ways to piggy-back (for free):

Google's Gmail Solution
- o Teacher creates the main email account. (Ex: mrsmith@gmail.com)
- o Students can then piggy-back on it.
  - ▪ mrsmith+jdoe@gmail.com
  - ▪ mrsmith+student123@gmail.com
  - ▪ Mrsmith+anything@gmail.com
- o This provides a unique email address for each registration.
- o All email arrives in the teacher's main Gmail account!

Other Inbox (www.otherinbox.com)
- o Teacher creates main email root. (Ex: mrsmith.otherinbox.com)
- o Students can then piggy-back on it.
  - ▪ jdoe@mrsmith.otherinbox.com
  - ▪ student123@mrsmith.otherinbox.com
  - ▪ anything@mrsmith.otherinbox.com
- o All mail arrives in one account (can be forwarded to another), separated into folders for each unique email address.

Copyright-friendly Image Sources

At of the time of this publication, the following websites contain images and allow students and educators to search for and use these images in projects under certain conditions. These conditions may change over time, so always be sure to check the site's terms of use.

Pics4Learning
http://www.pics4learning.com

"Copyright-friendly images for education." By far the most recommended site – contribute your own pictures and expand the library for all of us!

Free Foto
http://www.freefoto.com

Professional photographers sell their photos here. However, the usage agreement on the front page states: "Also non-commercial users may download our web size images to use off-line in school projects, church services, cards, leaflets, etc. Basically, if your off-line use is not commercial, you can download our web size images for free."

Some of the images are watermarked and navigation can be tricky!

Flickr (Creative Commons)
http://www.flickr.com/creativecommons

This is not necessarily a site you'd want students to use, but it's a great resource for you to gather images needed for projects. Though Flickr's guidelines state that inappropriate material cannot be posted on the site, every now and then you may find something that shouldn't be there. And who defines what "inappropriate" really means?

P D Photo (public domain)
http://www.pdphoto.org

Description from website: "PDPhoto.org is a repository for free public domain photos. Unless something is clearly marked as being copyrighted, you can assume it is free to use. But if you intend to use an image you find here for commercial use, please be aware that standards for such use are higher." The site has many different categories, but very heavy in landscapes and scenery.

Photo Home

http://www.photohome.com

Allen Matheson, a Texas photographer, has made his 72 dpi images available to educators and students for free (read the conditions at http://tinyurl.com/lua72p).

Gif.com
http://www.gif.com

Description from website: Search our collection of more than 17,000 quality free clipart images. No pop-ups, no tricks.

- This is a free offering from the parent company ClipArt.com (which is a paid subscription website).
- No login required.

Photos 8
http://www.photos8.com

Description from website: "This is a place for free public domain photos and desktop wallpapers. Large collection of High Resolution photos and wallpapers, Thousands of high quality public domain pictures, easy to search, All photos on Photos8.com are public domain. You may use these images for any purpose, including commercial. As the owner I have explicitly placed all the photos in the public domain. If you do use any photo, please consider linking back to this site or giving credit to this site. Just something like, "*Photo courtesy Photos8.com*." This is not required, but it's a very good way to support the site efforts here."

Library of Congress American Memory Museum
http://memory.loc.gov/ammem/index.html

The Library of Congress has great primary sources for you to use in your projects. Just because it's on a government website doesn't mean it's necessarily public domain. However, abiding by Fair Use guidelines, students should be able to use these resources.

National Archives
http://www.archives.gov/research/arc

There is more here than you ever imagined – and the number of digital resources is constantly growing!

Student Clip Art (hand-drawn from Sam Houston State University)
http://www.shsu.edu/~lis_mah/documents/clipartportal.html

Description from website: These images are primarily for the use of K-12 school students and teachers. All drawings are original works done by students or staff. All photographs are originals, taken by K-12 students and staff. This site is intended as a royalty free source of clipart for educational uses. If you use one or more of our images, we would like to hear from you.

Free Pixels
http://www.freepixels.com

Around 3,500 photos that can be used in your projects. No login required.

Stock.xchng
http://www.sxc.hu

Description from website: Whether you just want to browse our huge image gallery or want to share your own photos with others, this is the site for you!

Browse through the categories of our huge gallery containing over 350,000 quality stock photos by more than 30,000 photographers! Share your photos with fellow designers! SXC is a friendly community of photography addicts who generously offer their works to those who need them free of charge. If you have some nice photos that you'd like to share with others, join us!

- Great collection of photos
- Registration (free, email verified) required to download images
- Commercial images displayed first, so scroll down

WP ClipArt
http://www.wpclipart.com/browse.html

Description from website: WPClipart is a fast, clean and safe site for children and others to find good-quality, printable images that have no copyright restrictions. All the images are in the Public Domain. Ads on pages are minimal to make the site as fast as possible. While there are literally thousands of "fun" images – I take great pains to find, edit and retouch images of historical and/or general educational value.

Karen's Whimsy

http://karenswhimsy.com/public-domain-images

Description from website: On the following pages, you will find hundreds of beautiful images gleaned from my collection of old books, magazines, and postcards. They are all from material printed prior to 1923 and are in the public domain.

PublicDomainPictures.net
http://www.publicdomainpictures.net

Description from website: PublicDomainPictures.net is a repository for free public domain photos. You can upload your own pictures and share your work with others.

- No login required
- Browse by categories or use search features

everystockphoto
http://everystockphoto.com

Image search engine of sorts that displays the license of each image separately.

Free Digital Photos
http://www.freedigitalphotos.net

Description from website: All our photos are free for corporate and personal use. Every image is free, with an option to buy high resolution versions for use in print or graphic design.

Photo Express
http://www.photoxpress.com

Description from website: PhotoXpress is a high quality, royalty-free image bank that offers free digital images and illustrations to creative professionals. Our trusted network of photographers and partners continue to build the PhotoXpress image bank each and every day. Images from our collection may be used in brochures, advertisements, magazines, websites, etc.

Clipart Etc.

http://etc.usf.edu/clipart

Description from website: Every item comes with a choice of image size and format, as well as complete source information for proper citations in school projects. No advertisement-filled pages with pop-up windows or inappropriate links here. A friendly license (http://etc.usf.edu/clipart/license/license.htm) allows teachers and students to use up to 50 items in a single, non-commercial project without further permission.

Stock Vault
http://www.stockvault.net

Description from website: Stockvault.net is a stock photo sharing website where designers and photographers can meet to share their images. You don't have to sign up to be able to download our images, but we'd like you to do so anyway, just so you can gain access to our special features. All images on this site are free for personal and non-commercial usage.

Artvex
http://www.artvex.com

Terms from website: Permission is granted for limited non-profit personal use of up to fifteen (15) images from all categories. Moreover, credit is due on all published works.

Morgue File
http://www.morguefile.com/archive

Description from website: The morguefile free photo reference archive provides the public and creative community with a repository of free raw photo materials. These images can be used in your commercial or private projects.

Similar/Alternate Web 2.0 Sites
(for those used in this book)

While we believe we have chosen the best possible websites to use for the projects in this book, it may at some time become necessary to choose alternatives if our chosen sites become unavailable or impractical to use in the classroom setting. For this reason, we have assembled this list of similar and alternate websites. A more comprehensive list of Web 2.0 sites can be found on our blog at http://www.digitalgoonies.com.

Animoto
> http://www.onetruemedia.com
> www.magtoo.com
> www.rockyou.com
> www.slideroll.com
> www.slide.com
> http://www.moblyng.com/make-slideshow

Big Huge Labs Trading Cards
> http://www.says-it.com
> http://www.addletters.com
> http://www.redkid.net/generator/generator.php
> http://www.imagechef.com

TypeWithMe
> http://docs.google.com
> http://www.zoho.com

MixBook
> http://photopeach.com

ScrapBlog
> http://www.smilebox.com
> http://www.scrapo.com

TinyPaste
> http://pastebin.ca
> http://dpaste.com
> http://txtb.in

Voki
> http://www.readthewords.com
> http://www.vocaroo.com

Wordle
> http://tagcrowd.com
> http://tagxedo.com

the end of slideshows...

http://www.animoto.com

What is it?
From Animoto's own Press Release:

> Animoto is a web application that, with the click of a button, produces videos using images and music that a user selects. Using their patent-pending Artificial Intelligence developed to think like an actual editor and director, the resulting video has the emotional impact of a movie trailer and the visual energy of a music video.

Features
- Make beautiful videos in minutes, not hours.
- Premium access is granted to educators and students for free!
- Students register with a classroom code for free premium access.
- Students choose from a built-in music library.
- Videos are mixed and re-mixed with the click of a button.
- No overly complicated movie editing is necessary.
- Can retrieve photos from popular photo storage websites or upload your own.
- Embed videos into other websites, wikis, blogs, etc. or link directly to them.
- Videos can be downloaded to play offline.
- High-resolution version of the videos may be purchased for a small fee.

(See the sample videos on the enclosed CD.)

Precautions
- Premium access for students and teachers expires every six months, but can be renewed.
- Students must create accounts, each having a unique email address. (See the "Creating Accounts" section at the front of this book.)
- Videos can only be as long as one single song up to ten minutes or 10 MB.
- Individual photos may not exceed 5 MB in size.

User's Guide to Animoto

Applying for an All-Access Teacher Account
The Animoto company graciously provides educators and students free access to their premium content which will allow the creation of full-length videos. However, you must apply as an educator and wait for approval. This process can take several days.

1. Access http://animoto.com/education.

2. Click on the Apply Now button.

3. Fill in the form with the required information, then click the Submit Application button.

4. Wait for approval from Animoto. Upon approval, they will email you a message with a classroom code and helpful links.

   This classroom code will be valid for approximately six weeks and must be redeemed before it expires. Any account created using the classroom code will provide six months of free premium access. After this six-month period, you must re-apply for another All-Access (premium) code.

   If after a week you have not received your classroom code, email theguys@animoto.com for assistance.

Creating Accounts for Students (notes for teachers)
In order for students to register for their own All-Access (premium) account, they will need a classroom code (see previous section) and a unique email address (see the "Creating Accounts" section at the front of this book). With these two things in hand, they can proceed with the registration process using the Student Registration Sheet on the following page.

If you allow students to "piggy-back" on your email address, the accounts are under your control and students should use a birth date other than their own that reflects the age of the account owner being over thirteen years old.

Many districts prohibit students from giving out personal information when registering for such sites. Therefore students should create their own pseudonyms (fake names) to use for such sites or you may assign these to students.

Student Registration Sheet

www.animoto.com

Protecting your private information (such as your real name and birthdate) is an important part of staying safe on the Internet. For this reason, you will not use your real information to register for an account at the Animoto website. This guide will help you during the registration process.

1. Access the registration page at **https://animoto.com/sign_up**.

2. Fill out the email address you will use for the Animoto website. This email may be provided to you by your teacher.

   Email address for registration: _____

3. To protect your privacy, you will use your pseudonym (fake name) to fill out the About Me section. This pseudonym may also be provided by your teacher.

   Pseudonym: _____

4. For the date of birth, use the date of birth according to your teacher's instructions since this may not be your own.

   Date of birth to use for registration: _____

5. Enter the classroom code. This is case-sensitive, so enter it exactly as given to you by your teacher.

   Your classroom code: _____

6. Click the sign-up button once the required information has been entered.

Starting a new Video Project

1. The first time you register, you may click the **Create Video** button in the upper right corner to begin a new project.

2. To begin a new project on return visits to Animoto, click the **Create Video** link at the top of the page.

   If you had begun a project previously and not completed it, Animoto would display that project and this message:

   We've loaded the last project you were working on.   CLOSE ✕
   If you'd rather ditch this one and start a new project, click here.

3. Select the video type. In almost all cases, you will select the full-length video. The "animoto short" option only allows for a quick, 30-second video with a limited number of images.

After selecting the "full-length" option, you should automatically be taken to the Upload Images screen. If Animoto displays the following message, you must either create a new account with the All-Access code provided to you by your teacher or you must re-apply to have your premium access restored (premium access for students and teachers expires six months from the date it was granted).

You have no full-length video credits in your account   CLOSE ✕
To create a full-length video purchase credits. Alternatively, select "Animoto Short" to create a free 30-second video.

Uploading Images

1. On the Get Images screen, you may choose one of three options:

    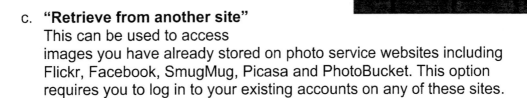

    a. **"Upload from your computer"**
        This will allow you to add images that are stored on your computer to the image collection for the video. You will almost always select this option.

    b. **"Select from our collection"**
        The images in the Animoto collection are more for title and credit slides that center around specific occasions.

    c. **"Retrieve from another site"**
        This can be used to access images you have already stored on photo service websites including Flickr, Facebook, SmugMug, Picasa and PhotoBucket. This option requires you to log in to your existing accounts on any of these sites.

2. After clicking the **Upload** button, navigate to the images you have stored on your computer that you want to upload and use in your Animoto video.

    You may select multiple image files by pressing the Ctrl key on the keyboard, then selecting the files you want.

    Click the **Open** button when you are ready to upload the selected photos.

    Note: Your screen may look much different than what is shown here.

3. It may take several minutes for all of your images to load. Once they are finished uploading, you will see the thumbnail images in the editing grid.

4. At any time, if you need to upload more images, simply click on the **Add More** button and repeat steps 1-3.

Adding Animoto Title Slides
After adding images, add title slides to help narrate or tell the story of your video. Animoto allows you to create text slides and add them directly into the editing grid.

1. Click on the **Add Text** button at the bottom of the editing grid. Notice that a text box thumbnail is immediately added to the editing grid.

2. In the details pane on the right side of the screen, add the Title and Subtitle you want displayed on the text slide.

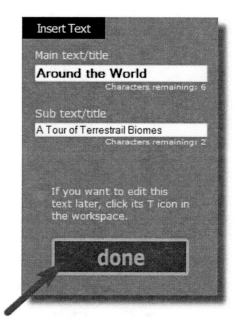

3. Click the **Done** button to save the changes to the text slide.

   The options for text are limited. The title will be displayed in white text on a black background. You have no control over the font size, type, or alignment. In addition, you are limited to 22 characters for the title and 30 for the subtitle.

   To create titles with complete control over the font, appearance, and alignment, see the next section titled "*Creating a Custom Text Slide Using PowerPoint.*"

4. At any time, you may edit the Animoto text slide by clicking on the text slide thumbnail in the editing grid, then making changes in the details pane.

Creating a Custom Title Slide Using PowerPoint

While Animoto allows you to create a title slide quickly and easily, it is very limited in features – lacking the ability to control the font, color, alignment, and appearance. For this reason, you may choose to create a customized title slide using a graphics or slideshow application. The following steps show how this is accomplished using Microsoft PowerPoint 2007.

It is easiest to make all the title/text slides for your whole project at one time so these steps will only need to be followed once.

1. Start a new, blank PowerPoint presentation.

2. On the first slide, right-click on the slide and select "**Format Background**."

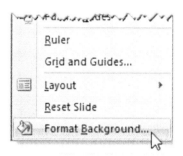

3. Click on the color fill bucket in the Fill properties window and select a background color.

About background colors:

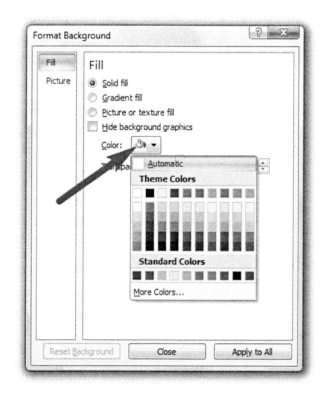

- Dark colors tend to look best (black is great).

- Stick to one background color for all title slides to build harmony.

4. Click the **Apply to All** button once the color is selected.

5. Click the **Close** button to return to editing your slide.

6. Click inside the **Title** box on the slide.

7. On the **Home** tab, click the **Font Color** button to change the font color. Note that a white font on a black background shows well. Select a color from the palette.

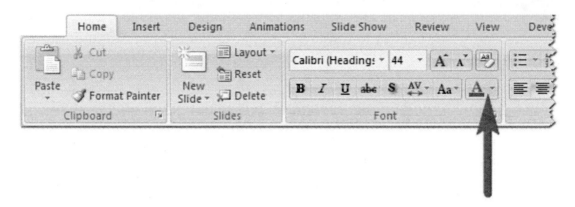

8. Type the text for your title slide into the textbox.

9. You may make other changes to the text. First, the text must be selected by highlighting it. Once the text is selected, consider making changes such as:

    1. Font type
    2. Font size
    3. Bold or Italics

10. You may delete any other blank textboxes that may be on your slide by clicking on the <u>border</u> of the empty textbox, then pressing the delete key on your keyboard.

11. If desired, you may rotate the textbox by clicking on the green handle and moving your mouse in a circular direction.

    Note: Keep the textbox away from the edges of the slide, as this may cause your text to get cut off when the Animoto video is created.

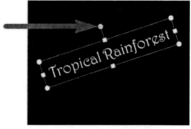

12. Add additional slides if needed for additional Titles. Repeat steps 6 – 11 as needed to make your title slides.

Tip: Once you have the first slide created, you can duplicate the slide, then simply change the text as needed on the new slide. To duplicate a slide, right-click on the slide (in the left pane) and choose "Duplicate Slide."

13. When you have finished creating the title slides, you must save them in .jpg format to use them in Animoto. You can save each slide as its own .jpg file with the following:

a. Click on the **Office** button then select "**Save As.**"

b. The default format for PowerPoint is .ppt or .pptx, but the slides must be saved as .jpg files. In the "**Save as type**" drop-down list, select **JPEG File Interchange Format**.

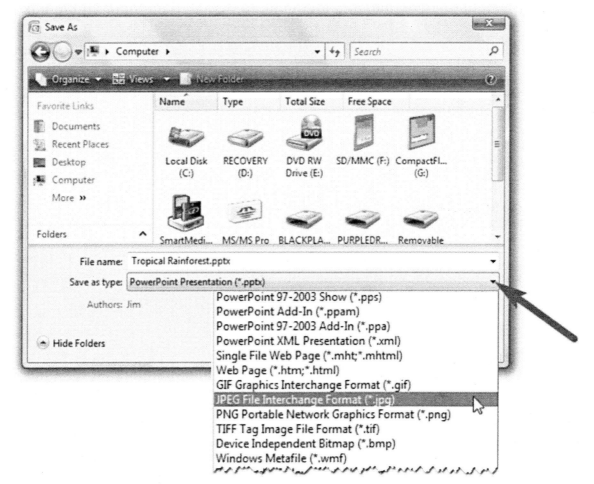

c. Enter an appropriate file name.

d. Select the location where you want to save the files.

e. Click the **Save** button.

    f. On the next screen, click the **Every Slide** button to save all your slides as .jpg files all at once.

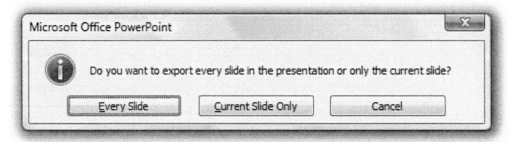

    g. A confirmation window like this one will verify that the slides have been saved as images and will tell you where they have been saved.

Note: The slides have been saved into a new folder in the location you selected in step 13d.

Now that the files have been saved, return to Animoto and add these as you would any other image.

Editing Images
Once images have been added, they can be rearranged and manipulated in the following ways.

    1. Sequence the images and title slides. The images will be mixed into the video in the order they appear in the edit grid from left to right and from top to bottom.

        a. Click on the image that you want to move and keep holding down the mouse button. A blue frame will appear around the image.

        b. Drag the image to where you want it to appear and release the mouse button. The other images will move to make room for the image you are moving.

2. Delete any images that are not needed.

    a. Click on the image that needs to be deleted. A blue frame will appear around the image.

    b. Click the **Delete** button on the toolbar.

    c. Confirm that you want to delete the image by clicking **OK**.

3. Rotate any images that are not oriented correctly.

    a. Click on the image that needs to be rotated. A blue frame will appear around the image.

    b. Click the **Rotate** button on the toolbar to rotate the image ninety degrees in a clockwise direction.

You may need to click the rotate button again until the image is oriented correctly.

Tip: Landscape images display much better in Animoto than portrait-oriented pictures (which must be rotated).

4. Spotlight the important images/title slides to make them stand out from the rest in the video. These will stay on the screen longer than the others in the completed video.

    Note: Title slides that are created within Animoto cannot be spotlighted and will automatically display longer than the others. Title slides made in PowerPoint (or other programs), will need to be spotlighted. If you do not spotlight these, they will not be displayed on the screen long enough for viewers to read during the playback of the video.

    a. Click on the image that needs to be spotlighted. A blue frame will appear around the image.

Tip: You may select multiple images by holding down the Ctrl key on the keyboard while clicking on each image.

    b. Click the **Spotlight** button on the toolbar to spotlight the selected image(s).

    c. A yellow frame will appear around all spotlighted images.

Adding Music

Adding music to a video project is simple in Animoto. You may either upload music from your own computer (MP3 format only) or select from Animoto's collection.

 Just because you have legally purchased or downloaded a song does not necessarily give you the rights to use that music in this manner. Typically, the use of such songs would need to meet the test of Fair Use (see http://www.copyright.gov/fls/fl102.html) according to copyright law. Because this can often be very confusing, we suggest using Animoto's library of music or using music in the Creative Commons or Public Domain.

1. Click the "**Select from our collection**" button on the Add Music screen.

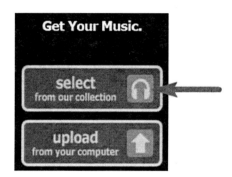

2. Choose a genre by clicking on one of the buttons in the list.

3. Use the following controls to preview/select a track or to return to the genre list.

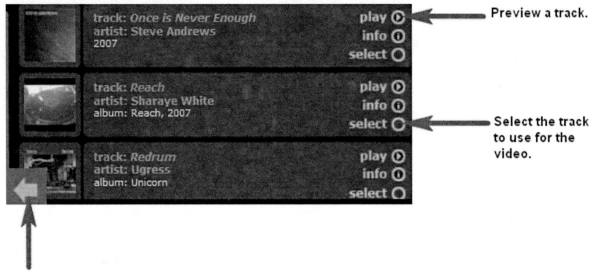

Preview a track.

Select the track to use for the video.

Return to the list of genres.

4. You may pause any music preview by clicking the **pause** button beneath the player in the details pane (on the right side of the screen).

Be sure to listen to (or read) all the lyrics of your chosen song, as it may have some content that is not appropriate for a school project.

5. Once you are satisfied with your music selection, click the **Save & Continue** button to proceed. You may first change the starting point of the music in your video if desired.

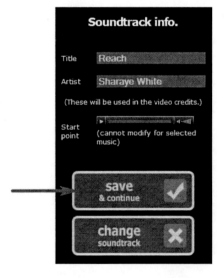

Finalizing the Video

Once music and images have been added to the project, the video must be "mixed" by Animoto. If you need to return to the screens to add/edit either images or music, click on the appropriate side tab. The following steps will mix your video.

1. Choose the image pacing you desire (half speed, normal speed, or double speed). Normally, you will accept the default/normal speed and change this only when re-mixing, if necessary.

2. Click on either side of the thumbnail in the "**Video cover screen**" section. This will cycle through the images in sequence to allow you to choose a cover screen. This will be the image your viewers see as the video waits to be played.

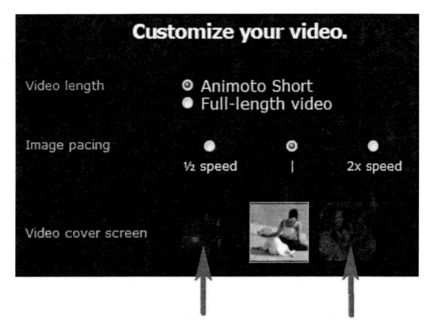

3. Click the **Continue** button to continue finalizing your video.

4. Fill in the information describing your video. This is the information viewers will see if they watch the video on the Animoto website (if you provide them a link to your video).

5. Click the **Create Video** button when you are ready to proceed.

6. Animoto will begin mixing your video and will display the following graphic, indicating that the mix is in progress.

This mixing process takes several minutes. At this point, you may navigate away from Animoto or close your browser entirely. An email will be sent to the address of the account to indicate that the video is ready. Or you may log back in to your Animoto account later to check and see if your video is ready.

Viewing Videos

If you remain logged in to Animoto while your video is mixed, the video will be displayed on the screen. Simply click on the video to start it.

If you have logged out of Animoto, your completed video will appear at the top of your My Videos list. Simply click on the **play** button next to the video title.

Re-mixing a Video

Once you have viewed the video, you may choose to re-mix the video. Each time the video is mixed, the transitions and appearance change drastically. Re-mixing does not delete the previous video.

1. Open the **Video Toolbox** by clicking on the button below the video.

2. Choose the **1-click Remix** to remix the video without changing the images or music. Choose **Edit** to make changes and re-mix.

Sharing Videos
There are three ways to share your video with others:
- Download the video as an mp4 file, then give the file to others.
- Provide a link (URL) to your video on the Animoto website.
- Embed the video into your own blog, wiki, or website.

Downloading the Video as an MP4 File

1. Open the video from your account where it can be played in Animoto.

2. Open the **Video Toolbox** by clicking on the button below the video.

3. Click the **Download** link in the Downloads column.

4. Click the **Save** button on the pop-up window. This will save the video to the default downloads location of whichever browser you are using.

Linking to the Video on the Animoto Website

1. Open the video from your account where it can be played in Animoto.

2. Select the URL in the address bar by **highlighting** with the mouse.

3. From the browser menu, select **Edit → Copy** (or use the keyboard shortcut Ctrl+C)

4. You may then paste the URL into an email message, instant message, document, blog, or other location where it can be shared with others.

Embedding the Video into another Website

Animoto videos may be embedded into most other websites, including blogs, wikis, and some social networks. This allows the video to play within these sites as an embedded player (or widget). Sites where the video can be embedded are too numerous to create specific instructions for each. However, each site requires you to paste the embed code. This embed code is automatically created by Animoto.

1. Open the video from your account where it can be played in Animoto.

2. Open the **Video Toolbox** by clicking on the button below the video.

3. Click the **Embed** button in the Sharing Tools column as shown.

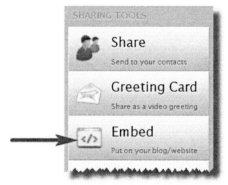

4. Choose the size of your embedded video by clicking on one of the three choices.

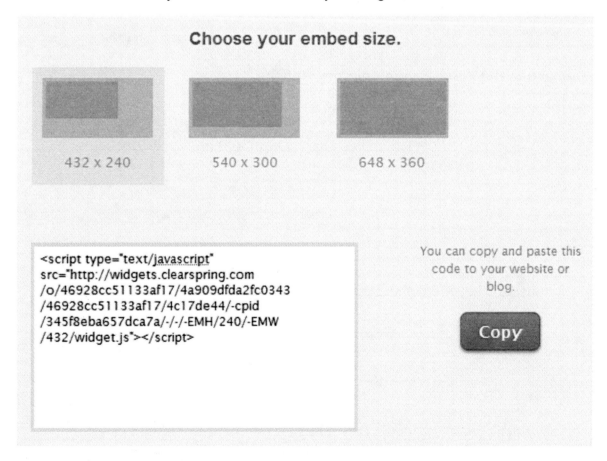

5. Click the **Copy** button to copy the displayed code into the clipboard.

Tip: Don't worry about what this code means! You don't need to understand the code – you only need to know how to copy the code from Animoto and paste it into your site.

6. Navigate to your website, blog, wiki, or other networked location and paste in the code following the site's individual instructions or requirements.

Some websites that allow embeddable content do not allow embed codes containing "script" tags – which is what is generated by Animoto. Script tags are often perceived as dangerous since some scripts are able to spread viruses and other malware.

Storyboard for Animoto Videos

Use this sheet as a guide for planning out both the content and sequence of your Animoto video. For any slideshow or video, always be sure to include a title slide (with your name) at the beginning, as well as a citation/credits slide at the end.

Animoto Format (circle one):   Short (30-second)   Full Length

Title Slide:

Text or Sketch:

Text or Sketch:

Text or Sketch:

Text or Sketch:

Text or Sketch:

Text or Sketch:

Text or Sketch:

Text or Sketch:

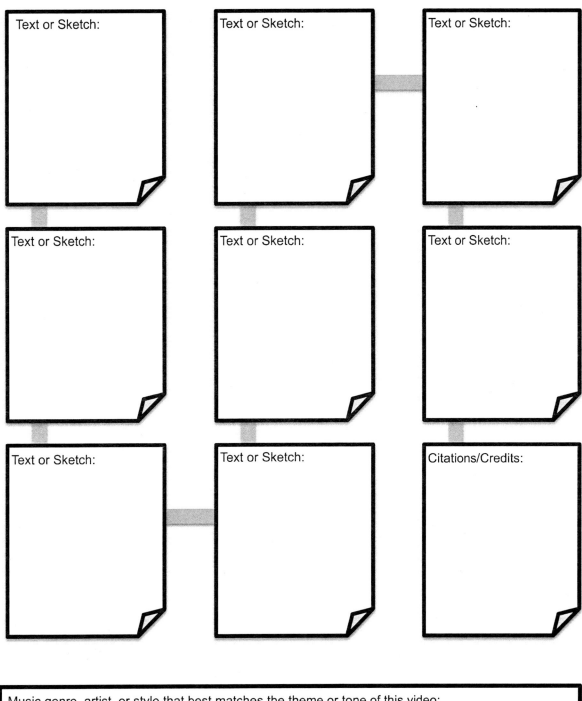

Text or Sketch:

Text or Sketch:

Text or Sketch:

Text or Sketch:

Text or Sketch:

Text or Sketch:

Text or Sketch:

Text or Sketch:

Citations/Credits:

Music genre, artist, or style that best matches the theme or tone of this video:

Big Huge Labs Trading Cards

Saturn

6th planet from the sun

Length of Year: 29.46 years (10753 Earth days)

Facts: Saturn is so light that it could actually ~~~ on water if there was an ocean big enough ~~~ has about 60 moons. Its rings ~~~ of pieces of rocks and d~~~

Photos f~~~

Stomach

Photo by missy & the univer~~~

In this organ, the stomach muscles grind the food and mix acid and other digestive juices with the food ~~~pieces to dissolve them. They must be broken down ~~~ny pieces so they can later be absorbed. ~~~ the universe.

Kilo- (k)

1000 X base unit

1 kilogram (km) = 1000 grams (g)
A newborn baby has a mass of about 3 kg.

Photo by Jim Holland.

Beaver

Found in streams and small lakes from Alaska to Mexico

The American beaver was driven to near-extinction in the 1800's due to overhunting. But the population has since rebounded. The beaver's tail helps it steer through water and works as a powerful paddle for extra speed. The beaver's teeth constantly grow throughout its life so it can gnaw on trees. (Photo by stevehdc. Information from Lincoln Park Zoo.)

http://bighugelabs.com/deck.php

What is it?

Big Huge Labs is a fun online image editor and generator that allows you to easily upload your photos and quickly turn them into magazine covers, posters, badges, desktop wallpapers and more. High resolution prints of the created images can be purchased for a fee. The digital images can be used for free in a variety of projects. While Big Huge Labs has a variety of image generators, the included lessons are limited to the use of the online Trading Card generator.

Features

- Can upload images from image hosting sites, from a URL, or from your own computer.
- No accounts or logging in required to create the trading cards.
- The digital images can be saved to use in a variety of projects, such as word processing documents, slideshows, or printed locally.
- A free Educator account allows for ad-free use of the site and the ability to create student logins without using student email addresses.
- No plug-ins required.

Precautions

- Ads on the page can be distracting to some students if you choose not to create student accounts.
- Images will be cropped automatically to fit into the area, so there is little control over the areas of the image that will be cropped.

User's Guide to BigHugeLab's Trading Cards

Creating a Teacher Account

The BigHugeLab's website is free, but ad-supported. This can be distracting to students. However, BigHugeLabs has created a way to avoid this. Teachers (with scanned proof of their employment) may apply for an Educator account (this is entirely optional and the site can still be used without creating accounts). This will allow teachers to create student logins with names, random IDs, and random passwords (all without student email accounts).

The advantages of using logins:
- Ads are removed.
- Student-created content is saved, so it can be viewed and downloaded.

To register for an Educator account:

1. Navigate to http://bighugelabs.com/education.php.

2. Click on the link to create a free account, then click OK, sign me up! .

> To enroll:
>
> 1. **Create a free account or sign in.**
> 2. Return here to scan and upload proof of current educator status. This can be a scan of your official school identification or similar document.

3. Fill out the information on the form, then click the **Save** button.

4. Return to http://bighugelabs.com/education.php.

5. Scan in proof of your Educator status (school ID or similar document).

6. Click the **Browse** button.

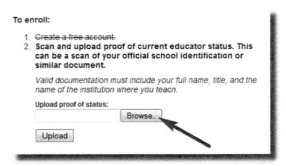

> To enroll:
>
> 1. ~~Create a free account~~
> 2. **Scan and upload proof of current educator status. This can be a scan of your official school identification or similar document.**
>
> *Valid documentation must include your full name, title, and the name of the institution where you teach.*
>
> Upload proof of status:
> [   ] Browse..
> Upload

7. Find your scanned proof, then click the **Open** button.

8. Next, click the **Upload** button.

9. Your information will be reviewed promptly and you will receive email notification upon approval.

Creating Student Accounts

Once you have received notification of approval for your Educator account, you may begin creating student accounts.

1. Return to the BigHugeLabs main page at http://bighugelabs.com.

2. Click the login link in the upper right of the window, then enter your username and password for the site.

3. Click the **My Account** link in the upper right of the site.

4. Now click on the **Students** tab.

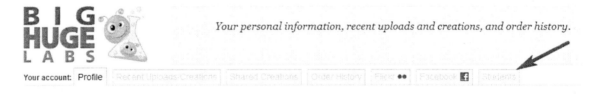

Your personal information, recent uploads and creations, and order history.

5. Add the student names as directed, then click the **Add Students** button.

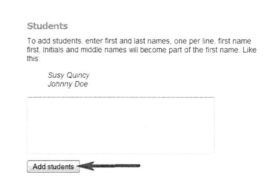

Students

To add students, enter first and last names, one per line, first name first. Initials and middle names will become part of the first name. Like this:

Susy Quincy
Johnny Doe

Add students

6. The student(s) will be added to your list. You may then print ID cards with the student information using the provided link or click "**View Details**" for an individual student's ID and password.

Click here to download all of your student data including IDs and passwords in a spreadsheet (CSV format).

Click here to create sheets of ID cards that can be printed and cut out. Each card has the student name, ID, and password. After clicking, just print the web page to print your ID cards.

Students use their ID and password to sign on.

Name	ID				
Student 1	93776897	View details,	Edit,	Reset password,	Delete
Student 2	34680458	View details,	Edit,	Reset password,	Delete
Student 3	68609553	View details,	Edit,	Reset password,	Delete

Creating Trading Cards

1. Navigate to http://bighugelabs.com/deck.php.

2. Click on the **Upload** tab, if necessary.

3. Click the **Browse** button to locate the image to use for the trading card.

4. Navigate to the folder or location where your image is stored.

5. Select the image and click the **Open** button.

6. Next, choose which part of the picture you want to keep if the picture needs to be cropped.

Keep this part of my photo visible if it must be cropped:
◉ Center   ◯ Top/Left   ◯ Bottom/Right

7. Select the style of the card by clicking on a button next to a color/style.

Choose a color for your card:

8. Even though the title, sub-title, and description fields are optional, fill them in according to the given directions. A completed card shows you how the text will look on the card.

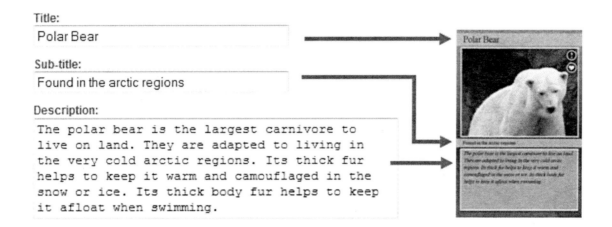

Title:
Polar Bear

Sub-title:
Found in the arctic regions

Description:
The polar bear is the largest carnivore to
live on land. They are adapted to living in
the very cold arctic regions. Its thick fur
helps to keep it warm and camouflaged in the
snow or ice. Its thick body fur helps to keep
it afloat when swimming.

Tip: You may add up to nine or ten lines of text in the description field. After this, the text will expand beyond the areas intended for text to display and will detract from your card's appearance.

9. You may select up to seven symbols to include on your card. To select a symbol, click on the **blank circle** then choose one of the symbols from the pop-up grid.

10. Click the **Create** button to create the trading card.

11. Once the card has been created, you may select an option below the image to edit the image or save the image.

12. If you are going to copy the image to paste into a document (such as Microsoft Word or Microsoft PowerPoint), right-click on the image and select **Copy** or **Copy Image**.

13. Switch to the application into which you want to place the image, then select the paste option (usually Edit → Paste or Ctrl+V).

Invite anyone to a pad by simply sharing the URL.

People currently viewing the pad show up in the sidebar.

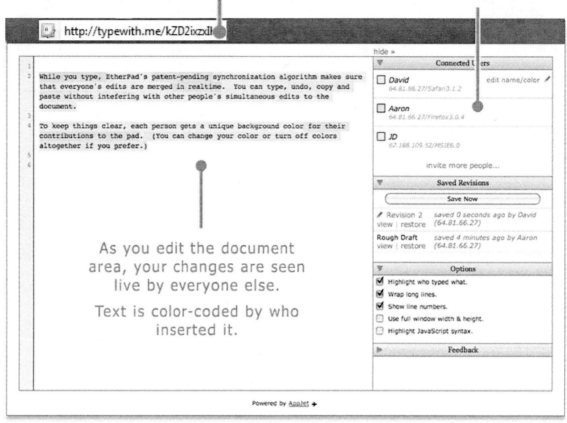

As you edit the document area, your changes are seen live by everyone else.

Text is color-coded by who inserted it.

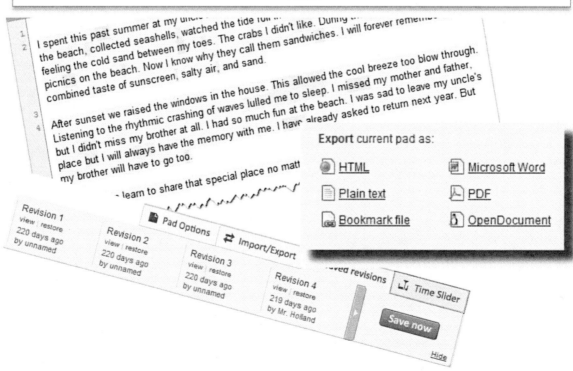

Export current pad as:

- HTML
- Plain text
- Bookmark file
- Microsoft Word
- PDF
- OpenDocument

Will You TypeWith.me?

http://typewith.me/

What is it?

TypeWithMe (formerly Etherpad) is a web-based word processor that allows multiple users to work on the same document in true real-time. Each user in the document chooses a highlight color so that any edits that user makes are highlighted in that color. The document is simultaneously refreshed on all users' screens without the lag in refresh time experienced with other online collaborative word processors.

Features

- Real time collaboration with no lag time
- Create your own URL for each pad (in the format www.typewith.me/yourURL)
- Can import/export in various text formats (Word, PDF, HTML, RTF, etc.)
- Each user's contribution is highlighted with a unique color
- Infinite number of revisions can be saved (and reverted)
- Built-in chat feature allows users on the same pad to communicate
- No accounts or logging in required (for the free, public version)
- No plug-ins required

Precautions

- Once a pad (a document) is created, it is present on the web forever.
- TypeWithMe offers no security – anyone who knows the URL of the pad can easily access it, edit it, and chat with other users of the pad.
- The highlight colors will not copy and paste into a word processor – this is limited to text only.
- If a student clicks the "Clear Authorship Colors" button, all highlighting will be removed.
- When the editor's name is changed on a pad, this name is stored as a cookie on the machine. This means that the next person using TypeWithMe on that machine will have the name of the previous user as a default.

User's Guide to TypeWithMe

Creating a Pad

To create a blank pad with a <u>random</u> URL, click on the blue banner on the start page.

To create a blank pad with a <u>customized</u> URL, simply type in the URL ending after the main TypeWithMe address of <u>http://typewith.me/</u>

Examples: <u>http://typewith.me/anything</u>
                          <u>http://typwith.me/mrsmith</u>
                          <u>http://typewith.me/writingproject15</u>

Sharing Your Pad

Anyone who enters the URL of your pad into a browser (or clicks a link pointing to the URL) can join your pad and begin editing. To share your link, copy the URL of the pad (in the browser's address window) and give it to whomever you need to share it with. You may do this by:

- pasting the link into an email message
- pasting the link into a shared document
- pasting the link into an instant message
- posting the link on a website
- writing it on paper and handing it off

Before Editing

1. Enter your name in the name field as indicated, then press the Enter key.

2. Click on the colored square and select an available color. If a color is already selected by another editor in the pad, select a different color.

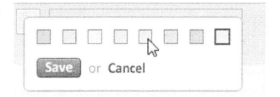

Editing the Document

1. Click in the document to set your cursor in the desired location.

2. Enter text. As you type your text, it will be highlighted with your chosen color. The characters you type will appear on the screens of the other users in your group in real time.

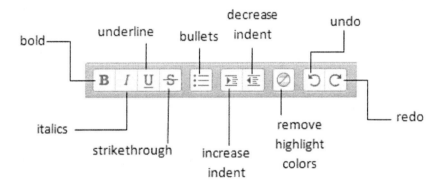

3. Advanced editing options can be accessed via the toolbar above the text area:

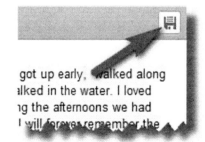

Saving Versions of your Work

1. To save your work periodically as you type, click on the save icon to save a "snapshot" of your project at that time.

2. To "revert" your project back to one of the saved versions, click on the Saved Revisions button. You may then select one of the previously saved revisions to view.

3. You may then choose to view a previous version or restore the current project back to a previous version. *NOTE: Before restoring your project to an earlier version, it is always a good idea to save the current version, then restore back to a previous one.*

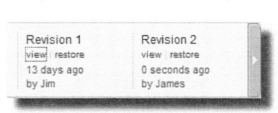

Exporting your Final Draft

Most likely, you will want to export your TypeWithMe project into another format that can become part of another project or file that can be turned in to your teacher. You have several options for exporting. To access these options, click on the Import/Export button.

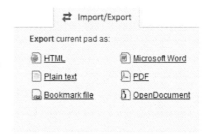

HTML – Choose this option if you want your text to be saved as a webpage that can be opened and viewed by a web browser such as Internet Explorer, Firefox, or Safari. This format is not easily edited.

Plain Text – This format will save the file in a .txt format. This can be opened and edited by nearly all basic word processors including Notepad, Word, Works, Simple Text, and many more.

Microsoft Word – This will create a .doc file that can be opened and edited with Microsoft Word or other Microsoft Office compatible software. If you have Microsoft Word available to you, this choice will provide you the most options for editing.

PDF – This option will create a PDF file (portable document format) that can be opened and read with programs such as Adobe Acrobat. Choose this format if you do not need to make any additional edits to the text outside of TypeWithMe.

Open Document – The .odt format is similar to the .doc format, but can be opened and edited by the Open Office productivity suite. Choose this option if you need to make additional edits to the text and you use Open Office (available for free from http://www.openoffice.org/).

Copy & Paste – Though this is not an option in the Import/Export tools, you may simply highlight the text in TypeWithMe (Ctrl+A to select all text), then switch to your program of choice and paste the text.

Regardless of the export option you choose, the highlighted colors will not transfer with the text. Should you need a snapshot of the text with the highlighted colors, you would need to create a screenshot (see the Wordle section of this book for screenshot instructions).

Aluminum (Al)
Soda cans, license plates, watercraft

NOVA SCOTIA
ABZ-87
CANADA'S OCEAN PLAY

Older gravestones are made of sandstone. Coal is used to provide electricity. Chalk is made of lime....

Sedimentary

Seeing... Our eyes observe colors, motion, and shapes.

I see a double rainbow.

The biome has long, warm, dry winters and wet and warm summers.

GRASSLAND

Wheel & Axle

Mixbook
Create beautiful photo books online.

http://www.mixbook.com/

What is it?

Mixbook is an online application that allows students to create books together by combining original photos with various backgrounds, layouts, and stickers to create a unique book centered around a central curricular theme. This book can be freely shared electronically in a smooth flash-based format (embedded or linked), or printed hard copies can be purchased to keep and share offline.

Features

- Multiple students can collaborate on the same book.
- Photos can be imported from various photo-hosting services or uploaded from a computer.
- Automix feature can create a book quickly from selected photos.
- Includes over a hundred layouts ranging from text only up to 21 pictures per page.
- Around 200 backgrounds which can be further customized.
- Photos and text can be edited and manipulated with basic, familiar tools.
- Posting an electronic book is free!
- Additional pages can be added and sequenced as needed.
- Books can be marked as private so only those invited can view books.

Precautions

- Logins are required for each user.
- Students under the age of thirteen must use an account created by a parent or guardian and have explicit permission to use the site. (See more about creating accounts for students in the introductory section of the book.)
- Many photos gathered from online sources will not be of high enough quality for printing – these will be indicated with a caution sign in the book editor.

In addition to the following instructions, the Mixbook tutorial may be accessed at http://www.mixbook.com/main/tutorial.

User's Guide to Mixbook

Creating an Account

In order to create any Mixbook, students must have an account. Students under the age of thirteen must use an account created by a parent or guardian and have explicit permission to use the site. (See more about creating accounts for students in the introductory section of the book.)

1. Click on the **Signup** link.

2. Enter a full name, email address, and password.

To protect student privacy, students should select a pseudonym (fake name) to use with Web 2.0 tools! Avoid using your real name!

Starting a New Mixbook

Once you create a new account, you will be prompted to fill in your profile information. This is not necessary. Click on the "**Create one now**" link to begin a new Mixbook.

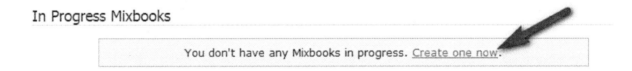

1. Fill in the basic information about the book. Only the title is mandatory. The rest of the information is optional and can always be changed later.

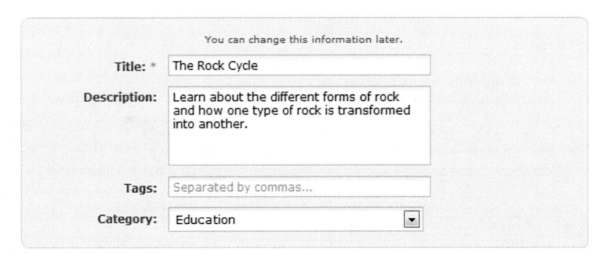

2. Set the view permissions. By default, only your Mixbook friends can view the project. Keep in mind, that even with "Only Friends" selected, anyone will be able to see your Mixbook on a site (such as a blog or wiki) where you have embedded the code from this Mixbook. This setting only applies to searching for or viewing Mixbooks within the Mixbook.com website.

3. Invite others to collaborate with you on the same Mixbook by entering their email addresses. If you already have collaborated with other students on a previous project, their names will appear in your friends list and you may invite them by selecting their names.

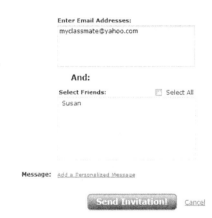

4. Click the **Create Mixbook** button when ready to begin editing.

5. Select the **size** for your Mixbook. The chosen size does not affect the size of the online Mixbook.

6. Choose a **theme** if desired. In most cases, you will select "I don't want to choose a theme."

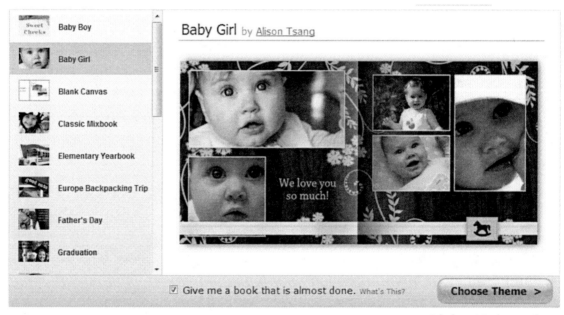

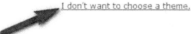

Resume Editing a Mixbook
Once you log in, the page will display any Mixbooks that you have in progress. To edit a Mixbook, simply click on the **Edit** button beneath the Mixbook's cover image.

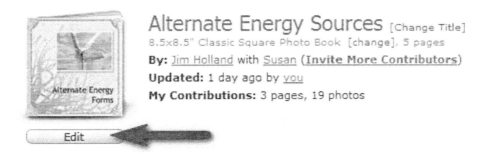

Uploading Photos to My Photos

When first creating a Mixbook, the first screen after choosing a theme will allow you to add photos to your Mixbook. You can access this screen any time by clicking the **Add Photos** button.

While Mixbook allows you to upload photos from various photo storage websites, in most cases you will upload your own or those you have legally obtained from other sources. Always keep in mind copyright regulations and fair use guidelines when obtaining images to use in your projects.

1. Click on the **Select Photos** button.

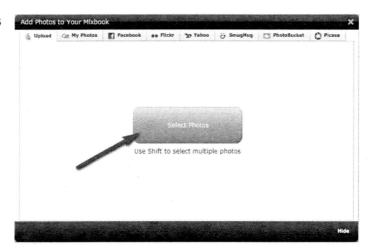

2. Navigate to the location of the files and select those you desire to include in your project. You may select multiple files by pressing the Ctrl key while selecting the images.

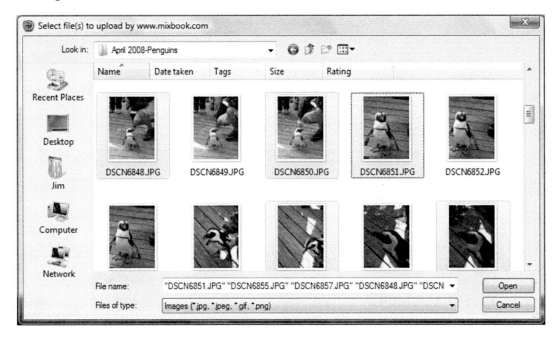

Once the images are selected, click the **Open** button. This will add the images to your "**My Photos**" area within Mixbook, but not to the current Mixbook itself. You may repeat this process as necessary. Close the photo upload screen when you are finished.

Adding/Removing Pages

By default, your Mixbook is created with a front and back cover and several pages in between. You may, at any time add, duplicate, or remove pages by using the **Page Tools** buttons as shown.

Tip: To make all pages consistent in their appearance, you may choose to create a complete page with an appropriate background and layout and then duplicate that page as many times as needed.

Selecting the Background

Solid colors and photo backgrounds can be added to each page, as well as the front and back covers. See the tip above about creating consistency in your book. Remember, the background should not detract or take away from the content on the pages.

1. Click on the **specific page** in the bottom ribbon for which you want to select a background.

2. Next, choose the **Backgrounds** tab.

3. To add one of the recommended backgrounds, simply click on the background's thumbnail image and it will be applied to the selected page.

   If the **Recommended Backgrounds** aren't showing, click on the **triangle** next to the group label as shown.

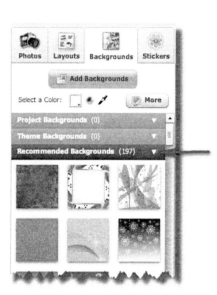

To add a solid color background, you may use the (a) color palette, (b) color mixer, or (c) color picker tool.

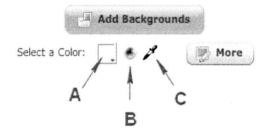

Editing the Background
Once solid colors and/or picture backgrounds have been added, you may edit the background to make small changes. With the desired page selected, these changes may be made.

Flip the Background

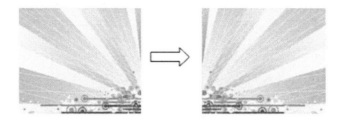

- This only applies to photo backgrounds. Pressing this button will flip the background across the **vertical** axis.
- Click the **More** button, then check the **Flip Background** box.

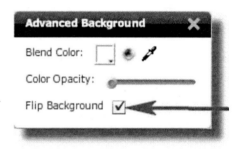

Change the Opacity

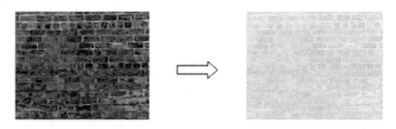

- Opacity refers to an item's transparency.
- Click the **More** button, then move the **Color Opacity** slider to make the image more transparent.
- This will not affect solid fill colors by themselves.

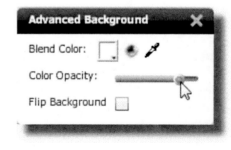

Tip: Try adding a background image and a solid fill color to the same page, then adjusting the opacity. This will give the appearance of tinting the background image with a desired color.

Selecting Layouts

After creating an appropriate background, select the layout for the page.

1. Click on the **specific page** in the bottom ribbon for which you want to select a layout.

2. Next, choose the **Layouts** tab.

3. The layouts are grouped according to the number of pictures desired in the layout.

   a. Click the **triangle** next to the group label to expand the group and see all the possible layouts.

   b. Click on a **layout icon** to select it. As soon as it is selected, the layout will be applied to the current page.

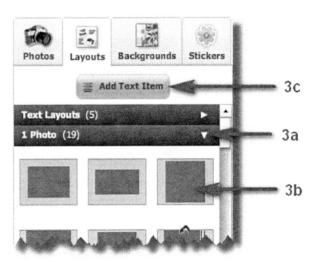

   c. If you simply need to add a text box, click the "**Add Text Item**" button.

Adding/Editing Photos & Stickers

Adding a Photo to a Photo Frame in the Layout

1. Click and drag a photo from the Photos collection and place it on top of the placeholder until the placeholder turns gold.

2. Release the mouse button to drop the image. The photo will automatically rotate and resize to fit the placeholder.

Adding a Photo or Sticker to any area of the Layout

To add a photo or sticker to any area of the layout, simply click and drag the item from the library at the left and drop it where desired.

Editing the Photo or Sticker

Once photos or stickers have been added, you may make adjustments to tweak the appearance. With the desired photo or sticker selected, these changes may be made.

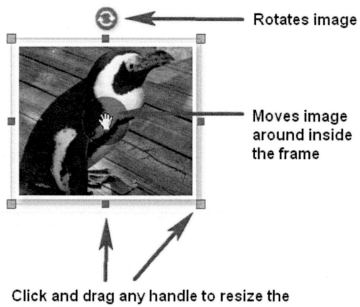

Rotates image

Moves image around inside the frame

Click and drag any handle to resize the photo frame

More Advanced Editing

Zooms photo in and out within the frame

Adjust styles for the image

Spans the image across two pages

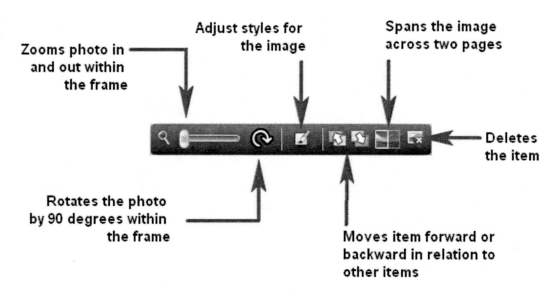

Deletes the item

Rotates the photo by 90 degrees within the frame

Moves item forward or backward in relation to other items

Editing Image Styles

With the photo selected, click the **Styles** button to make these edits.

- By hovering your mouse over each of the icons in the style window, you can preview how the style will look when applied to the selected image.

- Notice that the styles have multiple pages from which to choose.

- Three of the four styles have a Customize menu to further edit the style.

Adding/Editing Text

Text can be added to any layout and then edited accordingly.

1. To add text to an existing text box, simply click inside the text box and begin typing (double-click on existing text if necessary). If you need to add a new text box to the layout, first click on the **Layouts** tab, then click the "**Add Text Item**" button.

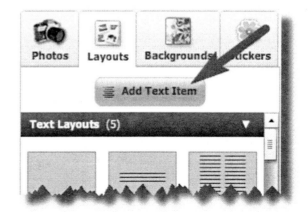

   The text box will then be added to the middle of the page where it can be further edited.

2. By default, the text is centered within the text box. The text box will grow as needed to accommodate the amount of text you enter. Once you enter the text, you may make the following edits.

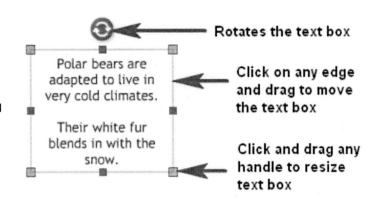

The following edits will be applied to the paragraph where the cursor is placed. If you want to apply the edits to all the text in the text box, you must first select the text by clicking and dragging the mouse over the text to highlight it.

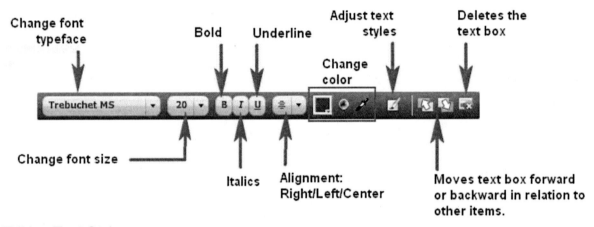

Editing Text Styles

The following effects can be applied to the text and text box.

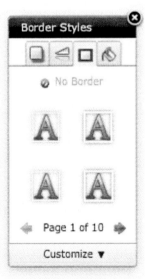

- By hovering your mouse over each of the icons in the style window, you can preview how the style will look when applied to the text box.

- Notice that the styles have multiple pages from which to choose.

- All four styles have a Customize menu to further edit the style.

Publishing the Book
Once the book is completed, it must be published in order to allow the book to be linked to or embedded.

1. Click the **Publish** button on the **editor** page.

2. Select the **Publish and Share** option.

3. You may change the Mixbook's title, description, and permissions. Click the **Publish Mixbook** button to continue.

Keep in mind that even with the "Only Friends" option selected, anyone will be able to see your Mixbook on a site (such as a blog or wiki) where you have embedded the code from this Mixbook.

4. Once the book is published, the online book will be displayed.

Sharing by Linking

To share your Mixbook by providing a link to others, simply copy the URL in the browser's address field and give it to others with whom you want to share your book.

Sharing by Embedding

The Mixbook may be embedded into another site, such as a blog, wiki, portal or personal website by embedding the provided HTML code.

1. On the page displaying the Mixbook, then click the **Share** button.

2. Next, choose the **Embed** link.

3. Depending on the site into which you are embedding the Mixbook, you may choose either the **MySpace** code or the code for "**Other Sites**." The "Other Sites" code uses  script tags, while the MySpace code uses Flash object tags. Since many wikis and other sites disallow the use of script tags (these can sometimes introduce viruses on these sites), it may be best to use the MySpace code, if possible.

4. Highlight the code and copy it by right-clicking on the highlighted code and selecting **Copy** from the menu.

For most blogs, wikis, websites, and portals you may simply paste this code in. For other sites you may have to first embed a widget to hold the code. There may be other requirements to format the code so that it will display the Mixbook properly on various sites.

Storyboard for Mixbooks

Use this sheet as a guide for planning out both the content and sequence of your Mixbook. For any slideshow or video, always be sure to include a title slide (with your name) at the beginning, as well as a citation/credits slide at the end. Rather than getting bogged down with the layout in this storyboard, simply plan which text and images you will include on each page.

Front Cover:

Page 1

Text to include:

Images to include:

Page 2

Text to include:

Images to include:

Page 3

Text to include:

Images to include:

Page 4

Text to include:

Images to include:

Page 5

Text to include:

Images to include:

Page 6

Text to include:

Images to include:

Page 7

Text to include:

Images to include:

Page 8

Text to include:

Images to include:

Back Cover:

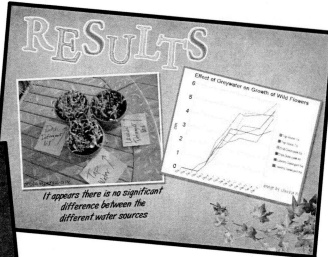

It appears there is no significant difference between the different water sources

Matter comes in three forms: solid, liquid and gas.

Adding a physical change such as temperature can change it to a different form.

Decomposers

Decomposers are organisms that eat the dead or decaying organisms. Fungi are the primary and most common of decomposers of litter in many ecosystems.

And poof... out comes a butterfly!

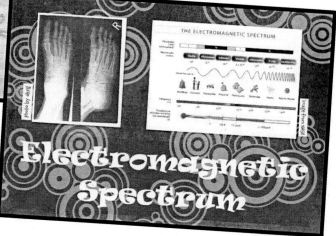

Electromagnetic Spectrum

http://www.scrapblog.com

What is it?

Scrapblog is an online scrapbook maker that allows the user to upload their own photographs, and then apply built-in backgrounds, stickers, frames and text to create one-of-a-kind layouts. Perfect for education, it allows students to create personalized projects limited only by their imaginations!

Features

- Although it's a freemium product, many of the backgrounds, stickers, etc. are free.
- Has built-in backgrounds, stickers, frames, fonts, music, etc. The user only supplies the photographs and the creativity!
- Scrapblog allows simultaneous logins from one account.

Precautions

- Uploaded images stay in the image library forever, or until you manually delete them one-by-one.
- Be sure to guard student's privacy. Scrapblogs should not contain personal information about students.
- Pages can be printed on your own printer free-of-charge, but they will not be full size.

User's Guide to Scrapblog

Creating an account

In order to save a Scrapblog, you must be logged in. It's easy to create an account; all you need is an email address. If your students have their own email addresses, they can set up an account of their own. However, they will have to make their Scrapblogs public, or invite you to view their Scrapblogs.

Another option is to set up a generic account for the entire class and let them log in with that one login. Scrapblog allows simultaneous logins, so each student can create their own Scrapblog and you don't have to worry about making their projects public.

1. To create an account, click on the **Log-in** button.

2. Click the **Create Account** button.

3. Create an Account with your email and password.

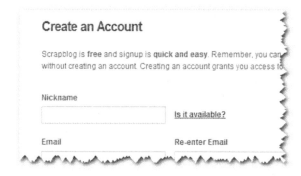

4. Log into your account.

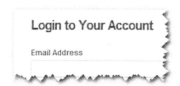

Starting a new scrapblog

1. Click on **Create New Scra**blog.

2. The next step is to decide whether to start with a theme or to start with a blank page. For most projects that kids are going to do, starting with a blank page will be the best choice.

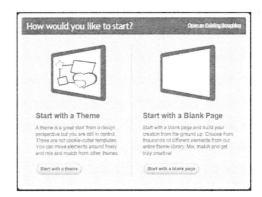

 **Remember to save periodically by clicking on the Save button near the top of the screen.**

Selecting photos

1. The first step is to get the photos. Click on the **Get Photos** button.

2. Photos can be added to your Scrapblog in several ways.
   a. Photos can be downloaded from several online photo storage locations: Photobucket, Flickr, Webshots, Facebook, Picasa, or Smugmug.
   b. Uploading pictures from a folder on your computer. Click the **Upload Photos** button and navigate to where the photos are stored. After you have selected the images you would like to use, click the **Start Upload** button.
   c. Selecting pictures already in the photo gallery.

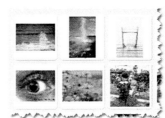

 Preloading images is a great way to use Scrapblog with younger students!

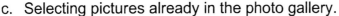

3. Click on the pictures you would to use in the project. They will "fly" into the left sidebar. When finished selecting photos, click **Done**.

4. To add photos to the project, drag them onto the center workspace.

5. To resize a photo, grab the corner "handles", and drag it larger or smaller.

6. To rotate a picture, grab the rotate arm and turn it to the desired angle.

Getting video

1. To get video, click on the **video** tab, then click on the **Get Video** button.

2. Video can be uploaded from one of two sources: Photobucket or YouTube.

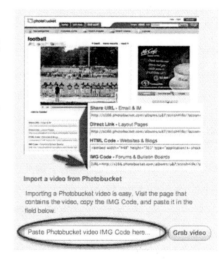

3. To use Photobucket, select the **Photobucket** tab and follow the directions in the pop-up box. Photobucket uploads require using the IMG code. Paste the code from the video into the box and click **Grab Video**. When you are finished, click **Done**.

4. To use YouTube, select the **YouTube** tab and follow the directions in the pop-up box. YouTube uploads require using the URL of the video. Paste the URL from the video into the box and click **Grab Video**. When you are finished, click **Done**.

5. When the video has been uploaded, it will appear in the left sidebar. Just drag it into your workspace to use. Video can be resized or rotated just like photos.

Selecting backgrounds

1. To select backgrounds for your project, click on the **background** tab. Click on **Get Backgrounds**.

2. Scrapblog is a **freemium** product, which means it's a combination of free and premium services. Scrapblog charges for some of the backgrounds, but many of them are free. Premium backgrounds are indicated with a coin symbol.

3. To find the free backgrounds, click on the **Least Credits** button. This will sort the backgrounds by cost, starting with the free backgrounds.

Newest | Popular | Least Credits

4. Another way to find backgrounds is to do a **keyword search**. Type a word in the search box to find backgrounds with a certain theme, such as butterflies or Halloween.

Search

5. Click on the backgrounds you would to use in the project. They will "fly" into the left sidebar. When finished selecting backgrounds, click **Close**.

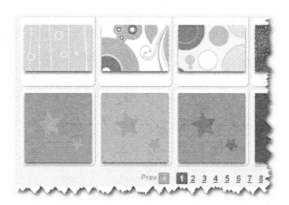

6. After backgrounds have been selected, they will appear in the left sidebar. Just drag the one you would like to use into your workspace. Changing a background is as easy as dragging a new background on top of the old background to replace it.

7. To use a photograph as a background, just drag it onto the workspace and resize to fill the entire space.

Adding text boxes

1. To add a text box, click on the **Text** tab. Decide which kind of text box you would like to have: a regular block of text, a thought bubble, or a speech bubble.

2. To place a box of text onto your workspace, just drag it onto the background.

3. Type the text into the box.

4. If a larger box is needed, drag the handles on the corners outward to fit the text.

5. The text can be customized by using the options in the **Edit** window on the right side of the workspace.

6. To select a different font, use the pull-down menu to choose one built into Scrapblog. Although Scrapblog doesn't allow you to upload your own fonts, there are more than 100 available in Scrapblog.

7. Text can be made bold, italicized, or underlined by highlighting it and then clicking the appropriate button.

8. To change the alignment of the text within a text box, just select the desired justification buttons.

9. To change the size of the text, click the size box and either type the desired size in the box or use the up/down arrows to adjust the size.

10. To change the color, click on the color button.

11. This dialog box will pop up. Pick the hue by sliding the arrows up or down the rainbow-colored slider.

12. Then select the exact shade or tint desired by moving your cursor around inside the color picker.

Pure black is in the lower right corner and pure white is in the upper left corner. The pure value of the selected hue is in the upper right corner and pure grey is in the lower left corner.

13. To sample a color from your Scrapblog (for example, to match the color in a photograph), click on the **sample** button. It will allow you to use the eyedropper to sample a color from within your Scrapblog. Just click on the color desired and it will appear in the color picker.

14. Custom colors that will be used often can be saved to the palate by clicking on the **Add to My Colors** button.

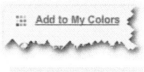

15. To add color to the text box itself, check the **Fill Color** box, and select a color with the color picker.

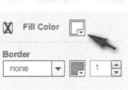

16. If a border is desired, select the style of the border: dashed line, dotted line, or a solid line. To pick the color use the color picker, and use the up/down arrows to determine the width of the border.

Stickers, frames and shapes (Embellishments)

1. Stickers, frames and shapes work pretty much the same, so use the following instructions for all three embellishments.

2. Scrapblog charges for some of the embellishments, but many of them are free. Premium products are indicated with a coin symbol.

3. To find the free embellishments, click on the **Least Credits** button. This will sort them by cost, starting with the free ones.

4. Another way to find stickers or frames is to do a **keyword search**. Type a word in the search box to find backgrounds with a certain theme, such as butterflies or Halloween.

5. Click on the embellishments you would to use in the project. They will "fly" into the left sidebar. When finished making selections, click **Close**.

6. To add stickers to the project, drag them onto the center workspace.

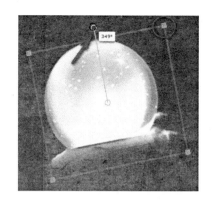

7. To resize a sticker, grab the corner "handles", and drag it larger or smaller.

8. To rotate a sticker, grab the rotate arm and turn it to the desired angle.

9. To use a frame on a photograph, grab the desired frame and drop it onto a photograph. Some frames go completely around a photograph, other are corner decoration only.

Overlapping

1. When two images, stickers or text boxes overlap, they may not be in the order that you would like. To change the way items overlap, click on the one of the items and then click on either the **Forward** or **Backward** button.

2. It may have to be clicked a few times depending on the number of items that may be overlapping.

   For example, clicking on the blue butterfly on the left and then the **Forward** button will make it move in front of the white butterfly on the right.

Adding new slides

1. To add a new slide, you can either duplicate an existing slide, or click on the **New Button** at the bottom of the page.

2. If you decide to add a new page, it will bring up a dialog box that will ask what type of page do you want. Select one of the types.

    a. **A Blank Page** is exactly that. You will then have to apply a background, text, stickers, etc.

    b. **From My Scrapblogs** gives you the choice to pick a page from any existing scrapblog that you have created in the past. It will copy it exactly, including the background, text, pictures and whatever else was on that page, even if those items weren't selected for the current project.

    c. **From a Theme** lets you choose from projects created by others with a certain theme in mind.

3. When you have the new page, you will either add new elements, or change the ones that already exist on the page. To delete an item, click on it and hit the delete button on your keyboard, or right-click and select delete.

Deleting a page

1. To delete an entire page, select the page you want to remove from the

thumbnails at the bottom, and select the **Delete** button.

Changing the order of the pages

1. If you would like to change the order of the pages, click on the **Reorder Pages** button. It will bring up a dialog box that shows thumbnail images of each page.

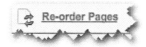

2. To move a page up in the order, click on the **up arrow** next to the slide. It will move up one place in the order. To continue moving it up, continue clicking the arrow until it is in the proper position.

3. To move a page down in the order, click on the **down arrow** next to the slide. It will move down one place in the order. To continue moving it down, continue clicking the arrow until it is in the proper position.

Adding transitions

1. To add transitions between slides when the Scrapblog is played, click on the **Transitions** button at the bottom of the screen.

2. Select one of the transitions available. To see what they will look like, click the **Preview** button to see a sample.

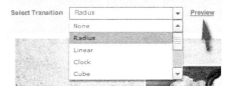

3. Decide if the transition will apply just to the selected page or to all the slides in your Scrapblog. Click **Done**.

Adding music

1. To add music to the Scrapblog, click on the **Music** button at the bottom of the screen.

2. To select music, use the pull-down menu to choose one built into Scrapblog. Although Scrapblog doesn't allow you to upload your own music, there are more than 30 selections available in Scrapblog.

3. Click the **Play** button to preview the music. Once you have selected, click **Done**.

Publishing

1. When you are finished with your Scrapblog, it is time to **Publish**.

2. Click on the **Publish** button.

3. This will bring up a dialog box where you will have to decide who can view your Scrapblog.

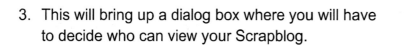

 If you make your Scrapblog public, then the entire world can find and view this Scrapblog. Please keep student privacy in mind. There should be no identifiable photos or other information about students. A safer way is to always make student projects private.

4. After you have marked your Scrapblog public or private, you will need to tag your Scrapblog. Add words that could be used in a keyword search. Be sure to separate each word or phrase with a comma. When you are finished, click **Publish**.

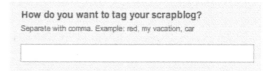

 Tip: Scrapblog can take a few minutes to publish, especially if there are a lot of pages in your Scrapblog.

5. When your Scrapblog is finished, it will give you a box with several choices.
    a. You can view your finished Scrapblog.
    b. You can print your Scrapblog as a book, a card, or a calendar. Additional charges do apply.
    c. Share your Scrapblog. Paste the supplied URL into an email or make a link on a website or blog.
    d. You can see other sharing options.

6. If you select **More Sharing Options** you will get this box with several other options.

7. If you choose **Share Elsewhere**, you can select where you would like to post this Scrapblog. Each one will have you log in and will then give instructions about how to post to their pages.

8. If you choose **Copy and Paste** it will give you a unique URL to copy and place in an instant message window, in an email, or on a webpage.

9. If you choose **Send to a Friend**, it will ask you to type in email addresses or will allow you to import from an email service such as AOL, Yahoo, Outlook Express, Gmail, or Plaxo.

Editing an existing Scrapblog

1. To edit an existing Scrapblog, go to Scrapblog's main page.

2. Click on **My Scrapblogs** near the top of the page.   My Scrapblogs

3. Your Scrapblogs will be shown on the left side of the page, with the newest ones on top. Scroll to find the one you want.

4. Click on the **Edit** button, which will reopen the Scrapblog Builder. You can then make as many changes to the Scrapblog as you like and will republish your Scrapblog when you are finished.

Legs

Adult insects have 6 legs. Each segment of the thorax has one set of legs. The legs are segmented. Often the last segment of the leg has a small claw.

photo by HVargas

New Version

Cell Membrane

a thick, rigid semi-permeable membrane that surrounds a plant cell. This layer of cellulose fiber gives the cell most of its support and structure.

New Version

Mouse

photo by Stephen Barnett

The mouse is eaten by http://tinypaste.com/91b

New Version

Bunsen Burner

A small laboratory burner connected to a gas source and producing a very hot flame.

photo by tsuihin - Timo Studios

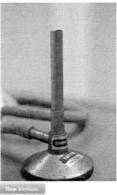

New Version

http://www.tinypaste.com

What is it?

TinyPaste is a pastebin, also known as a nopaste, a web application that allows its users to upload snippets of text, usually samples of source code, for public viewing. In other words, TinyPaste is a service that allows you to combine text, images, and video into one posting with a small (Some might say tiny!) URL.

Features

- No accounts or logging in required.
- You can type as much text as you want without limits.
- Supports bold, italics, underlined, or strikethrough text.
- Can change the color or size of the text.
- Can include images, video and links to websites.

Precautions

- Once a document is published it is present on the web forever.
- All information is publicly viewable.
- Need to understand just little bit of html code to edit text with color, size, or style.
- Images and videos can only be added as long as they are hosted online.
- Videos are only available from specific locations.

The TinyPaste® name, logo, and screenshots are used with permission and do not imply any endorsement of the lessons, activities, or methodologies in this publication on the part of TinyPaste™.

User's Guide to TinyPaste

Creating a TinyPaste

Go to www.tinypaste.com.

Click in the box to type your text. You can also paste text from other sources.

Editing the TinyPaste

To use the bold, italics, underline, strikethrough, color, or size buttons, you have to understand just a little about **html code**. TinyPaste doesn't use true html code, but a similar version. In order to make a certain section of the text bold, or have red letters, or be really large, you have to use the code buttons. When you click on the buttons, or select a certain color or size, TinyPaste will put in a set of html tags. For example, if I click on the **bold** button, I get these tags: [tpb] [/tpb]. The first tag tells the computer to turn on bold text, and the second tag tells it to turn it off.

"I [tpb] love [/tpb] pizza" would look like this: I **love** pizza.

The same thing is true for the color and size selections. [tpsize=6] tells the computer to make the font a size 6 (out of 7, which is pretty large!) and [/tpsize] telling it to stop making the font a size 6. Here's how that would look:

"She [tpsize=6] really [/tpsize] loves pizza" becomes: She

really loves pizza.

Edit your text using the bold, italics, underline, or strikethrough buttons as needed.

Click the appropriate button, then type the text between the html tags.

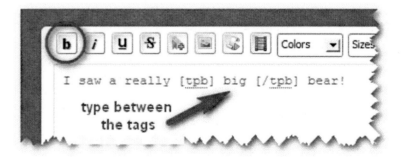

Changing the font size or color is as
easy as clicking on the **color** or **size**
buttons and then typing inside the
html tags.

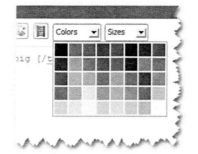

type the part that should be
resized inside the html tags

Adding a link

To add a link to a website, click on the **Link** button.

This dialog box will pop up to type the website
into. Type the **URL** of the website. Click **OK**.

Then this dialog box pops up. If you would like to
have a different text appear on the post, you can
type it in the box. Click **OK**.

Adding an image

To add an image to the post, you can click the **Insert Image** button.

This dialog box will appear. Enter the **URL** of the location of the image. Click **OK**.

To get the URL of an online image, (Firefox) right-click the image and select **Copy Image Location**. This will give you the URL of the image, not the entire webpage.

Adding a video

To add a video to the post, you can click the **Insert Video** button.

This dialog box will appear. Select the location of where the video is stored. Another dialog box will ask for the location of the video. You can usually get the URL of the video by right-clicking on the video and selecting properties.

Finishing the posting

At any point during this process you can preview the posting. Click **Preview Paste** to see how the final result will look.

When you are satisfied with the posting, click **Submit** to convert it to a TinyPaste.

TinyPaste will provide you with a link to your posting, condensed into a short URL. **Copy your URL** and use it in places where only a short piece of text would work.

☑ **Entry Added!**

http://tinypaste.com/becc4

http://www.voki.com

What is it?

Voki is a web-based application that allows users to express themselves on the web, with their own voices, using talking characters. Characters can be personalized to look like the user, famous people, or even animals or monsters. The user's voice can be recorded with a microphone, over a telephone, or synthesized using a wide variety of voices built into the application to convert text to speech.

Features

- Wide variety of character choices and personalization available.
- No accounts or logging in required.
- Output can be embedded into blogs, website, or other online media.
- Free. (At least at this time!)
- Stored online, no specific platform required.

Precautions

- Students will spend as much time as you give them selecting a character and the accompanying clothing and bling. Limit their selection time, or force them to "roll the dice" to pick a character.
- Voki can be embedded into another media or can be emailed to an email account.
- Voki requires Internet access to create and view.
- There is no way to "download" the Voki.
- A voki cannot be edited unless saved to an registered (but free) account.

The Voki® name, logo, and screenshots are used with permission and do not imply any endorsement of the lessons, activities, or methodologies in this publication on the part of OddCast Inc.™.

User's Guide to Voki

Creating a Voki

1. Go to www.voki.com.

2. Click "**Get Started**."

3. Click on the **Head** icon of Customize Your Character.

4. Scroll through the different categories of characters to find one you like.

5. Click on the one you want to select it.

This process could take an entire computer lab class. Some students may spend an hour or more just looking at all the choice and customizations. Set a timer to keep students on track.

Tip: Another option, if time is limited, is to have students "roll the dice" to select a character. Limit the number of rolls, or set a short period of time such as three minutes to allow students to select a character.

Customize your character

1. Under the **Head** tab, you may find choices for hair, mouths, facial hair, etc. Different characters have different choices.

2. The **Clothing** tab will have choices of clothes for your character. Most will have different shirts to wear, and some will also have hats.

3. The **Bling** tab will have glasses/sunglasses, jewelry, and possibly tattoos.

4. At any point during this process, you can tweak your character's facial features or coloring.

5. Click **Tweak**. Adjust the size of the eyes, nose, mouth, height, and width as desired.

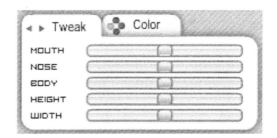

6. Click **Color**. Adjust the color of the mouth, eyes, skin and hair as desired.

7. When you are happy with the character you have created, click on the **Done** button at the bottom of the window.

Recording the voice

1. The next step is to give your character a voice.

2. There are four ways to do this: record a message by phone, type in the message and select a voice for Voki to speak for you, record your message with a microphone, or upload a saved audio file.

3. The first way is to record by phone. When you click on the phone icon it will bring up this dialog box. Type in your telephone number and click **Call Me**. Voki will call your phone. Answer it and follow the voice prompts to record your message.

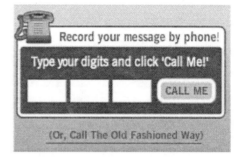

4. The second way is to type in your message. Type your message directly into the blue box, or cut and paste from another document. This method is best suited for short messages.

5. Select which language/accent and which specific voice best suits your character. To preview your choices, click the **Play** button. If some of your words are not pronounced correctly, you may want to edit your text to spell words phonetically.

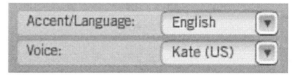

6. The third way to give your character a voice is to click on the **Microphone** button. To start recording, click the **Start** button. To stop, click the **Stop** button. Your recording is limited to 60 seconds. To preview your recording, click the **Play** button.

7. The last method of giving your character a voice is to upload a pre-recorded message. Compatible file types are .wma, .pcm, .mp3, and .wma. Browse for your file, select it, and click the **Upload** button.

8. When you are satisfied with the voice you have created for your character, click the **Done** button at the bottom of the window.

Selecting a Background

1. The next thing your character needs is a background. Click on the **Background** button. Select the category of background you would like. Move your character up or down as needed.

2. You can also upload a photograph of your own to be the background.

3. When you make a selection, click the **Done** button at the bottom of the window.

Select a Player

1. The last choice to be made is the color of the player.

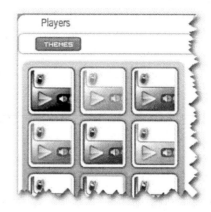

2. Select a color and click the **Done** button.

Publishing your Voki

1. Click the **Publish** button.

2. A dialog button will pop up asking you to name the scene.

3. Click **Save**.

4. This dialog box will pop up asking you to create an account. Click on **No, thanks**.

5. Click **Close**.

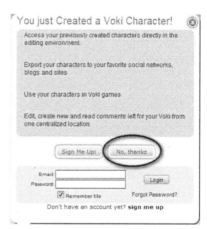

6. To embed in a webpage or blog, use
    one of the sets of code. You may have
    to experiment to see which one works
    best.

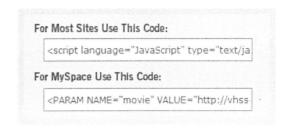

7. To get the direct URL to use in another type
    of project, email it to an email address. Then
    you can copy and paste the URL.

WORDLE

www.wordle.net

What is it?

Wordle allows students to create "word clouds" from text they provide. These clouds give greater prominence to words that appear more frequently in the source text. Students then can select different layouts, fonts, and color schemes to customize their "word cloud."

Features

- Customizable.
- Free to use.
- No accounts or logging in required.
- Wordles can be printed or saved to be used as part of another project.

Precautions

- The Wordle gallery isn't censored, so non-school appropriate content may be viewed on the Wordle gallery.
- When publishing to the gallery, be cautious about posting personal information than can be seen by others.
- There is no way to edit the words in a Wordle, so if a word is misspelled or words were left out, you will have to start over.
- Wordles cannot be saved directly, so a screen capture must be done to use a Wordle image in other projects.

The Wordle® name, logo, and screenshots are used with permission and do not imply any endorsement of the lessons, activities, or methodologies in this publication on the part of Wordle™.

User's Guide to Wordle

Creating a Wordle

 **When opening www.wordle.net, it displays the last four Wordles created and saved to the gallery. Please keep in mind that there is no way to censor work by others, and that some of these Wordles may not be school-appropriate for your students.**

A way to get around this is to go to: www.wordle.net/create, which will take students directly to the page to create their Wordles. Skip to step #2.

1. Click **Create** on the menu at the top of the page.

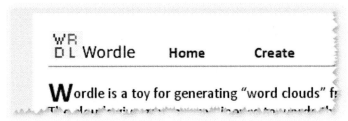

2. Type in text for the word cloud, or paste from another application. The size that a word is displayed is proportionate to the number of times it was used.

   For example, if I type "frog frog frog frog dog dog cat", dog will be twice as large as cat, and frog will be twice as large as dog.

3. To keep two-word phrases together, type the tilde (~) key between them. Such as "Girl~Scout" or "Spring~Break."

4. Click **Go**.

5. Wordle will display the word cloud.

Customizing the Wordle

1. To try a different arrangement, color, or font, click
   Randomize. This will give the word cloud a
   completely different look each time it's clicked.

2. For more control of how the word cloud looks, use the **Font**, **Layout** and **Color**
   buttons to give the Wordle a customized look.

3. To keep to keep from including common words, such as a, an, or the, go to
   Language – Remove Common English Words.

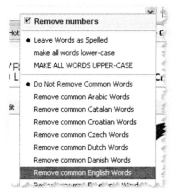

4. Under the **Language** menu, there are also choices to make all words upper case, or make all words lower case.

> **Tip: To make the words outlined in black and white, saving color ink on the printer, double-click the Wordle. Students can then use crayons or markers to color the words.**

Printing and Saving Wordles

1. To print the Wordle, click the **Print** button and select the printer. The Wordle will print out nicely on a page by itself.

2. To save as a .pdf, you will need a program that makes PDFs. A couple of free versions that work nicely for this purpose are CutePDF or PrimoPDF. Click the **Print** button and select the PDF maker as the printer, then click **OK**.

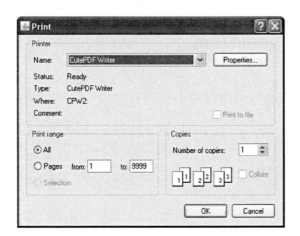

It will bring up a dialog box that asks where to save the document. Select the correct location to save and click **Save**.

3. Wordle does not have the ability to save directly as an image. It is a Java Applet which cannot write directly to your computer. In order to save as .jpg or a .gif, the student will need to take a screen capture, either using the **Print Screen** command or Screen Capture software.

 **Things to Keep in Mind!**

1. Wordle doesn't save anything to a server unless you choose to save to **Public Gallery**. Wordle doesn't require an account. The user selects a title for the Wordle, selects a user name, or uses the default "Anonymous," and can give a short description if desired.

2. When publishing to the gallery be cautious about posting personal information, particularly with student information. If a Wordle is created without posting to the Public Gallery, the information cannot be seen by others.

3. Wordle does not collect information about the user. Wordles are created by frequency of words, sentences, or paragraphs cannot be reconstructed.

4. Wordle images are licensed under a Creative Commons Attribution License. They can be used for any purpose, including commercial uses, but images must be attributed to www.wordle.net.

Online Samples of Lessons

Animoto

Characteristics of Living Things
http://animoto.com/play/FG3SQ8rSCx9LP3uBGPwnGQ

Energy Forms
http://animoto.com/play/yydzzwmoQiXIGn5kw0dhuQ

Natural Disasters
http://animoto.com/play/96HyMWu8to6H5ixEvKyYoA

Plant Foods
http://animoto.com/play/dHLB8e0VVH0SMNbVXqt2lg

Water Cycle
http://animoto.com/play/ixsNplygf77F5mwoo8vMzw

Mixbook

Biomes
http://www.mixbook.com/photo-books/all/terrestrial-biomes-4526139

Elements (Common Uses)
http://www.mixbook.com/photo-books/all/common-uses-of-elements-of-the-periodic-table-4555989

Five Senses
http://www.mixbook.com/photo-books/all/the-five-senses-4555946

Rock Cycle
http://www.mixbook.com/photo-books/all/rock-cycle-4555987

Simple Machines
http://www.mixbook.com/photo-books/all/simple-machines-4555028

Scrapblog

Butterfly Life Cycle
http://www.scrapblog.com/06414457-4702/0BE5C22D-BC11

Electromagnetic Spectrum
http://www.scrapblog.com/06414457-4702/58B50BB1-1FB7

Producers, Consumers and Decomposers
http://www.scrapblog.com/06414457-4702/55B8802D-5BFD

Science Fair
http://www.scrapblog.com/06414457-4702/31CDE9F7-71B0

States of Matter
http://www.scrapblog.com/06414457-4702/37D336A9-660C

TinyPaste

Cellular Organelles
http://tinypaste.com/0f70b

Food Chain
http://tinypaste.com/bf5a3

Insects
http://tinypaste.com/cbde8b0

Tools of Science
http://tinypaste.com/7ff69b5

Voki

Dinosaurs
http://www.voki.com/php/viewmessage/?chsm=697d5a946deff8b96802b600717c65cd&mId=349565

Forces of Nature
http://www.voki.com/php/viewmessage/?chsm=e0fcb531efeeddd54a955a6559c08a5b&mId=349463

Moon
http://www.voki.com/php/viewmessage/?chsm=eca49a02354a317f4519fee1bc8a546a&mId=349579

Photosynthesis
http://www.voki.com/php/viewmessage/?chsm=f6ecfba27b3873271454aada5a73c3dc&mId=349586

Tides
http://www.voki.com/php/viewmessage/?chsm=72b054c1553fc50fce884465b8499c52&mId=349590

Student Activity
TypeWithMe: Scrambled Lab Report

Grade Level: Content Area(s):
Intermediate Science (5-8)

On CD-ROM:
LabReportSAS.pdf
LabReportSAS-key.pdf
LabReportGroupDirections.doc
ScrambledLabReportText.doc
ScrambledLabReportText-key.pdf

Lesson Overview:
Students will collaborate with two or three other students to re-write a lab report that has been mysteriously mixed up. For this, they will use TypeWithMe – an online tool that will allow students to see exactly what other students in the team are typing as they type. Students will first practice classifying statements according to the specific step of the scientific method to which each belongs. Using TypeWithMe, students will then edit the scrambled lab report by moving sentences into a logical sequence following the scientific method. These statements also contain grammar and spelling errors which must be corrected. Finally, students will export their collaborative documents, make any necessary adjustments, then turn in or print for assessment purposes.

Software or Special Materials/Supplies:
Student Activity Sheet
Web browser (Firefox recommended)
Microsoft Word (optional)

Standards:
NSES 5-8 Content Standard A
- Different kinds of questions suggest different kinds of scientific investigations.
- Current scientific knowledge and understanding guide scientific investigations.
- Scientific explanations emphasize evidence, have logically consistent arguments, and use scientific principles, models, and theories.

Science TEKS

(Grades 3-8)
2.a-e: The student uses scientific inquiry methods during laboratory and field investigations. The student is expected to:
  a. plan and implement comparative and descriptive investigations by making observations, asking well-defined questions, and using appropriate equipment and technology.
  b. design and implement experimental investigations by making observations, asking well-defined questions, formulating testable hypotheses, and using appropriate equipment and technology.
  c. collect and record data using the International System of Units (SI) and qualitative means such as labeled drawings, writing, and graphic organizers.
  d. construct tables and graphs, using repeated trials and means, to organize data and identify patterns.
  e. analyze data to formulate reasonable explanations, communicate valid conclusions supported by the data, and predict trends.

Procedures:
This lesson should follow a brief introduction of the steps of the scientific method and is intended to reinforce concepts that have already been introduced.

Before Computer Work Begins

1. Print the necessary sections of the *User's Guide to TypeWithMe.*
2. Create as many TypeWithMe pads as necessary to accommodate each group of three or four students. For security reasons, it is best to use the "Create Public Pad" button which creates an obscure URL for each pad.
3. Write or type the URL for each group on the LabReportGroupDirections.doc document .
4. Decide on the final format of the document to be turned in. Edit *Step Four* of the directions sheet to reflect this (and print the directions, one for each student, making sure the groups contain no more than four students).
5. Paste the text from the LabReportText.doc file into each pad, then save the TypeWithMe pad.
6. Distribute the Student Activity Sheet and explain to students that they will be working as a team to fix a scrambled lab report. But first, they must practice classifying steps of the scientific process into the specific steps of the scientific method. Allow plenty of time for students to complete this activity on their own.
7. Divide the students into groups of three or four and distribute the Group Directions half-sheets.
8. Allow students ample time to read the directions.
9. Reiterate the TypeWithMe rules with the students, being sure to explain your policy on using the built-in chat. This chat feature can be both very helpful and very distracting.
10. Explain to students how they will save their completed projects and turn them into you – and in which format (ex: Word, PDF, Plain Text).
11. Distribute the *User's Guide to TypeWithMe* to students.

Computer Activities

1. Remind students of the requirements for this project as stated on the Group Directions sheet.
2. Guide students in starting a browser and navigating to the specific URL assigned to them.
3. You, as the teacher, should be a member of each TypeWithMe pad to monitor the session.
4. Direct students in editing/entering their names and colors on the open pad.
5. If necessary, show students the basic tools of TypeWithMe, including how to cut and paste and how to save the revisions of their projects.
6. Allow time for students to work.
7. When the first group is finished, demonstrate how to export the TypeWithMe text into the chosen format.
8. Lead students in saving their work and turning in their files or printing their text.

Name: _____   Date: _____

TypeWithMe: Scrambled Lab Report Student Activity Sheet

Before writing any lab report, it is necessary to first understand the steps and sequence of the scientific method. Each of the statements below belongs to a specific step of the scientific method. Classify each statement by entering the letter corresponding to the scientific method step as follows:

P = State the Problem
H = Form a Hypothesis
E = Conduct the Experiment
D = Collect & Analyze Data
C = State the Conclusion

	Step	Statement to Classify
Ex.	P	How much water is in a can of soda?
1		The results indicate that the water on the west side of town contains more minerals than the east.
2		The class mixed the two substances together for five minutes then measured the amount of light passing through it.
3		Based on an encyclopedia article I read, I say the mixture will turn green.
4		Our group boiled the solution for five minutes to allow plenty of time for the water to evaporate. The evaporated water was collected with an inverted funnel.
5		The heavier object will hit the ground first.
6		The class measured the plant growth daily and created a pictograph to show the rate of growth.
7		The experiment proved that the weight of the objects did not have any effect on how fast they fell to the earth.
8		Each group counted the number of insects in their given area.

9		How much light will UV coated sunglasses filter out?
10		Our tests indicate that hand sanitizers do not kill any more bacteria than hand soap.
11		I think the balloon with the warmer air will stay aloft longer.
12		Tony measured the amount of rainfall and graphed the results.
13		What is the impact of music on standardized test scores?
14		The warm water will float on top of the cold water.
15		How much nitrogen is needed for optimal plant growth?
16		Brenda measured the temperature of the two samples and recorded her results on a spreadsheet.
17		The boys placed a piece of bread in a zipped bag and stored it in a dark cabinet with a constant temperature.
18		What colors attract bees the most?
19		Juan filled the dishes with the same amount of water and placed one in the sun and one in the shade.
20		Susan and Gaby placed thermometers around the room at different elevations.

Group Members: _____

For today's activity, you will be collaborating with your peers to re-write a lab report that has been mysteriously mixed up. For this, you will use an online tool called TypeWithMe. This will let you see exactly what other students in your team are typing as they type. The rules for using this tool in class are as follows:

- Upon entering the TypeWithMe pad, edit your name as instructed by the teacher.
- Each person in the team must have a different color.
- Talking to one another verbally is prohibited.
- You may use the chat feature on the page only with the teacher's permission.
- Everything you write must be appropriate and on-task.
- Avoid typing over your peers – work on different sections of the document at the same time.

Assignment:

1. Access your group's TypeWithMe pad at: http://www.typewith.me/_____

2. Add the names of both group members at the top of the TypeWithMe pad.

3. Move the statements around (cut and paste) into the correct sections of the lab report to make comprehensive paragraphs. Be sure to correct any spelling or grammar errors.

4. Upon completion, export the TypeWithMe as a Word document. You may make additional edits if necessary. Save the Word document with your name in the file name and turn it in as instructed.

Group Members: _____

For today's activity, you will be collaborating with your peers to re-write a lab report that has been mysteriously mixed up. For this, you will use an online tool called TypeWithMe. This will let you see exactly what other students in your team are typing as they type. The rules for using this tool in class are as follows:

- Upon entering the TypeWithMe pad, edit your name as instructed by the teacher.
- Each person in the team must have a different color.
- Talking to one another verbally is prohibited.
- You may use the chat feature on the page only with the teacher's permission.
- Everything you write must be appropriate and on-task
- Avoid typing over your peers – work on different sections of the document at the same time.

Assignment:

1. Access your group's TypeWithMe pad at: http://www.typewith.me/_____

2. Add the names of both group members at the top of the TypeWithMe pad.

5. Move the statements around (cut and paste) into the correct sections of the lab report to make comprehensive paragraphs. Be sure to correct any spelling or grammar errors.

3. Upon completion, export the TypeWithMe as a Word document. You may make additional edits if necessary. Save the Word document with your name in the file name and turn it in as instructed.

Student Activity
TypeWithMe: Lab Safety Guidelines

Grade Level: Content Area(s):
Intermediate Science (5-8)

On CD-ROM:
LabSafetySAS.pdf
LabSafetyGroupDirections.doc
LabSafetyRulesMixup.doc
LabSafetyRulesMixup-key.pdf

Lesson Overview:
Students will collaborate with two or three other students to re-write a set of lab safety rules that have been mysteriously mixed up. For this, they will use TypeWithMe – an online tool that will allow students to see exactly what other students in the team are typing as they type. Students will first state and illustrate four chosen lab safety rules on the Student Activity Sheet. Using TypeWithMe, students will then edit the ridiculously mixed-up set of lab safety rules by re-writing them to make them true. These statements also contain grammar and spelling errors that must be corrected. Finally, students will export their collaborative documents, make any necessary adjustments, then turn in or print the documents for assessment purposes.

Software or Special Materials/Supplies:
Student Activity Sheet
Web browser (Firefox recommended)
Microsoft Word (optional)

Standards:
NSES 5-8 Content Standard A and B
- Scientific investigations sometimes result in new ideas and phenomena for study, generate new methods or procedures for an investigation, or develop new technologies to improve the collection of data. All of these results can lead to new investigations.
- Different kinds of questions suggest different kinds of scientific investigations. Some investigations involve observing and describing objects; some involve collecting specimens; some involve seeking more information; some involve discovery of new objects and phenomena.
- Technology used to gather data enhances accuracy and allows scientists to analyze and quantify results of investigations.

Science TEKS

(Grades 3-8)
1.a: The student conducts the classroom and outdoor investigations following school and home safety procedures and environmentally appropriate practices. The student is expected to demonstrate safe practices as described in the Texas Safety Standards during classroom and outdoor investigations, including observing a schoolyard habitat.

4.b: The student knows how to use a variety of tools and safety equipment to conduct science inquiry. The student is expected to use preventative safety equipment, including chemical splash goggles, aprons, and gloves, and be prepared to use emergency safety equipment, including an eye/face wash, a fire blanket, and a fire extinguisher.

Procedures:
This lesson should follow a lesson on lab safety that is specific to your needs.

Before Computer Work Begins

1. Print the necessary sections of the *User's Guide to TypeWithMe*.
2. Create as many TypeWithMe pads as necessary to accommodate each group of three or four students. For security reasons, it is best to use the "Click to Create a New Document" button which creates an obscure URL for each pad.
3. Write or type the URL for each group on the LabReportGroupDirections.doc document.
4. Decide on the final format of the document to be turned in. Edit *Step Four* of the directions sheet to reflect this. Print the directions, one for each student, making sure the groups contain no more than four students.
5. Paste the text from the LabSafetyRulesMixup.doc file into each pad, then save the TypeWithMe pad.
6. Distribute the Student Activity Sheet and explain to students that they will be working as a team to correct a set of lab safety rules. But first, they will brainstorm four lab safety rules that have already been taught and will create illustrations showing the rules being ignored. Allow plenty of time for students to complete this activity on their own.
7. Divide the students into groups of three or four students and distribute the Group Directions half-sheets.
8. Allow students ample time to read the directions.
9. Reiterate the TypeWithMe rules with the students, being sure to explain your policy on using the built-in chat. This chat feature can be both very helpful and very distracting.
10. Explain to students how they will save their completed projects and turn them into you – and in which format (ex: Word, PDF, Plain Text).
11. Distribute the *User's Guide to TypeWithMe* to students.

Computer Activities

1. Remind students of the requirements for this project as stated on the Group Directions sheet.
2. Guide students in starting a browser and navigating to the specific URL assigned to them.
3. You, as the teacher, should be a member of each TypeWithMe pad to monitor the session.
4. Direct students in editing/entering their names and colors on the open pad.
5. If necessary, show students the basic tools of TypeWithMe, including how to replace text and how to save the revisions of their projects.
6. Allow time for students to work.
7. When the first group is finished, demonstrate how to export the TypeWithMe text into the chosen format.
8. Lead students in saving their work and turning in their files or printing their text.

Name: _____   Date: _____

TypeWithMe: Lab Safety Student Activity Sheet

Choose four lab safety rules. For each rule, write out the text of the rule in a box below. Then create an illustration showing the rule **NOT** being followed in a lab setting.

Safety Rule:

Safety Rule:

Illustration:

Illustration:

Lab Safety

Safety Rule:

Safety Rule:

Illustration:

Illustration:

Group Members: _____

For today's activity, you will be collaborating with your peers to re-write a lab report that has been mysteriously mixed up. For this, you will use an online tool called TypeWithMe. This will let you see exactly what other students in your team are typing as they type. The rules for using this tool in class are as follows:

TypeWith.me

- Upon entering the TypeWithMe pad, edit your name as instructed by the teacher.
- Each person in the team must have a different color.
- Talking to one another verbally is prohibited.
- You may use the chat feature on the page only with the teacher's permission.
- Everything you write must be appropriate and on-task.
- Avoid typing over your peers – work on different sections of the document at the same time.

Assignment:

1. Access your group's TypeWithMe pad at: http://www.typewith.me/_____

2. Add the names of all group members at the top of the TypeWithMe pad.

3. Rewrite each statement to make it true and correct any spelling or grammar errors.

4. Upon completion, export the TypeWithMe as a Word document. You may make additional edits if necessary. Save the Word document with your name in the file name and turn it in as instructed.

Group Members: _____

For today's activity, you will be collaborating with your peers to re-write a lab report that has been mysteriously mixed up. For this, you will use an online tool called TypeWithMe. This will let you see exactly what other students in your team are typing as they type. The rules for using this tool in class are as follows:

TypeWith.me

- Upon entering the TypeWithMe pad, edit your name as instructed by the teacher.
- Each person in the team must have a different color.
- Talking to one another verbally is prohibited.
- You may use the chat feature on the page only with the teacher's permission.
- Everything you write must be appropriate and on-task
- Avoid typing over your peers – work on different sections of the document at the same time.

Assignment:

1. Access your group's TypeWithMe pad at: http://www.typewith.me/_____

2. Add the names of both group members at the top of the TypeWithMe pad.

3. Rewrite each statement to make it true and correct any spelling or grammar errors.

4. Upon completion, export the TypeWithMe as a Word document. You may make additional edits if necessary. Save the Word document with your name in the file name and turn it in as instructed.

Student Activity
TinyPaste: Tools of Science

Grade Level: Content Area(s):
Intermediate Science (5-8)

On CD-ROM:
ScienceToolsSAS.pdf
ScienceToolsSample.URL (shortcut to completed example – available only online)

Lesson Overview:
Students will use TinyPaste to create a textbin of tools used in science. Students will research the use of each tool, and will use a Student Activity Sheet to record this information. Students will also find an online image to illustrate the use of the tool, and will use the image and text to create a TinyPaste. Students can preview their TinyPaste and make revisions until they are satisfied with the final result. Students then can record the URL of their TinyPaste.

Software or Special Materials/Supplies:
Student Activity Sheet
Flash-enabled web browser (Firefox recommended)

Standards:
NSES 5-8 Content Standard A and C
- Different kinds of questions suggest different kinds of scientific investigations. Some investigations involve observing and describing objects; some involve collecting specimens; some involve seeking more information; some involve discovery of new objects and phenomena.
- Technology used to gather data enhances accuracy and allows scientists to analyze and quantify results of investigations.

Science TEKS

(Grades 3-8)
4.a-b: The student knows how to use a variety of tools and safety equipment to conduct science inquiry. The student is expected to:
  a. use appropriate tools to collect, record, and analyze information, including life science models, hand lens, stereoscopes, microscopes, beakers, Petri dishes, microscope slides, graduated cylinders, test tubes, meter sticks, metric rulers, metric tape measures, timing devices, hot plates, balances, thermometers, calculators, water test kits, computers, temperature and pH probes, collecting nets, insect traps, globes, digital cameras, journals/notebooks, and other equipment as needed to teach the curriculum.
  b. use preventative safety equipment, including chemical splash goggles, aprons, and gloves, and be prepared to use emergency safety equipment, including an eye/face wash, a fire blanket, and a fire extinguisher.

Procedures:
This lesson should follow a brief introduction of tools of science and is intended to reinforce concepts that have already been introduced.

Before Computer Work Begins

1. Distribute the Student Activity Sheets for students to plan their TinyPaste. You may want to consider assigning the Student Activity Sheet for homework or completing them in class the day prior to creating the TinyPaste. Allow students plenty of time to complete the activity sheet.
2. Students will need online images to complete this activity. Decide where they will obtain these images. (See the *User's Guide to TinyPaste*.)
3. Print the necessary sections of the *User's Guide to TinyPaste*.

Computer Activities

1. Remind students of the requirements for this project as stated on the Student Activity Sheet.
2. Guide students to http://www.tinypaste.com.
3. Lead students in beginning a new project, referring to the User's Guide as needed.
4. Demonstrate how to create a TinyPaste including adding an image, increasing text size to make a title, and adding text to describe the insect body part.
5. Lead students in saving and publishing the TinyPaste, including recording the URL.

Name: _____ Date: _____

TOOLS OF SCIENCE

When working in a science lab, there are many pieces of equipment. Each has a specific role – some to keep you safe, others to allow you to conduct experiments. Select 10 tools used in a science lab (ask your teacher for a list) and create a TinyPaste for each one. Include at least one image and tell how it is used.

Use this sheet as a guide to help plan for your project. In each box, fill in the appropriate information.   http://tinypaste.com

Name of tool	How tool is used	TinyPaste address

Student Activity
BigHugeLabs Trading Cards: Metric Measurement

Grade Level: Content Area(s):
Elementary/Intermediate Science (3-8)

On CD-ROM:
MetricMeasurementSAS.pdf
MetricMeasurementSample.pdf
Metric Measurement Images (folder)
Metric Mesurement Sample Cards (folder)

Lesson Overview:
Students will use the BigHugeLabs Trading Card generator to create a series of collectible cards, each having an image, title, subtitle, and descriptive text to illustrate and explain the use and value of the common metric prefixes. Students may either gather images from the Internet or other sources, or may use the ones supplied on the CD (especially if time is limited). Finally, students will save and share their completed trading cards in print format or by displaying them within a slideshow or document.

Software or Special Materials/Supplies:
Student Activity Sheet
Javascript-enabled web browser (Firefox recommended)
Resources for obtaining images (optional)

Standards:
NSES K-4 Content Standard A,B, and E
- Simple instruments, such as magnifiers, thermometers, and rulers, provide more information than scientists obtain using only their senses.
- Objects have many observable properties, including size, weight, shape, color, temperature, and the ability to react with other substances. Those properties can be measured using tools, such as rulers, balances, and thermometers.
- Tools help scientists make better observations, measurements, and equipment for investigations. They help scientists see, measure, and do things that they could not otherwise see, measure, and do.

Science TEKS

(Grades 3-4)
2b: The student uses scientific inquiry methods during laboratory and outdoor investigations. The student is expected to collect data by observing and measuring using the metric system and recognize differences between observed and measured data.

(Grades 3-8)
4a: The student knows how to use a variety of tools and methods to conduct science inquiry. The student is expected to collect, record, and analyze, information using tools, including microscopes, cameras, computers, hand lenses, metric rulers, Celsius thermometers, wind vanes, rain gauges, pan balances, graduated cylinders, beakers, spring scales, hot plates, meter sticks, compasses, magnets, collecting nets, notebooks, sound recorders, and Sun, Earth, and Moon system models; timing devices, including clocks and stopwatches; and materials to support observation of habitats of organisms such as terrariums and aquariums.

Procedures:
This lesson should follow an introduction to metric measurement and is intended for reinforcement and practice.

Before Computer Work Begins

1. To introduce this activity, show the completed sample (MetricMeasurementSample.pdf on CD).
2. Distribute the Student Activity Sheet and explain to students that they must create trading cards to explain the use and value of the basic metric prefixes.
3. Gather a list of resources that students may use to obtain information.
4. You may want to consider assigning the Student Activity Sheet for homework or completing it in class the day prior to creating the trading cards.
5. Decide whether students will be responsible for obtaining their own images or will use the ones provided on the CD. The images used on each of the cards should represent the common item for which students are giving an example measurement. For example, on the "Kilo" card, a student may state "A newborn baby has a mass of about 3 kg." An appropriate image would be that of a newborn baby. If students are using the images provided on the CD, upload these files to a shared network location, or distribute the files according to standard procedures.
6. Decide how the final trading cards will be shared and accessed. Students will either print their cards or embed the image files into a slideshow, such as PowerPoint, or into a word processing document.
7. Print the necessary sections of the *User's Guide to BigHugeLabs Trading Cards*.

Computer Activities

1. Remind students of the requirements for each card in this project as stated on the Student Activity Sheet.
    *   Title: Name of the metric prefix with the prefix abbreviation
    *   Subtitle: Value of the prefix
    *   A common measure that uses the prefix (ex: "A cup of coffee is about 1 deciliter.")
    *   Citations for the information and image source
2. Guide students in obtaining images, either from the ones supplied on the CD (which have been placed in a student-accessible location) or from various image websites (see the introductory section of this book for a list of some sites).
3. Guide students to http://bighugelabs.com/deck.php.
4. Lead students in beginning a new project, referring to the User's Guide as needed.
5. Demonstrate how to upload the image.
6. Walk students through the process of selecting cropping options and a background color.
7. Using the Student Activity Sheet as a guide, allow students time to enter the necessary text in the appropriate fields.
8. Guide students in selecting symbols to add to the card (if desired).
9. Demonstrate how to create the card and save or copy it to an appropriate location.
10. Once the collection of cards has been created and saved, give students specific instructions for printing or inserting into a document.

Name: _____   Date: _____

BigHugeLabs Trading Cards: Metric Measurement

For this activity, you will use the BigHugeLabs Trading Card generator to create **seven to ten** cards describing each of the basic metric prefixes. You must include the following on each card:

- Title: Name of the metric prefix with the prefix abbreviation
- Subtitle: Value of the prefix
- A common measure that uses the prefix (ex: "A cup of coffee is about 1 deciliter.")
- Citations for your information and image source

You will save the trading card images so that they can either be printed or embedded into another application, such as PowerPoint or Microsoft Word, according to your teacher's directions.

Use this sheet as a guide to help plan for your project. In each box, fill in the appropriate information. Depending upon your teacher's instructions, you may have a few blank boxes.

Metric Prefix #1:

- Value:

- Common Measure:

- Image Search Terms:

Metric Prefix #2:

- Value:

- Common Measure:

- Image Search Terms:

Metric Prefix #3:

- Value:

- Common Measure:

- Image Search Terms:

Metric Prefix #4:

- Value:

- Common Measure:

- Image Search Terms:

Metric Prefix #5:

- Value:

- Common Measure:

- Image Search Terms:

Metric Prefix #6:

- Value:

- Common Measure:

- Image Search Terms:

Metric Prefix #7:

- Value:

- Common Measure:

- Image Search Terms:

Metric Prefix #8:

- Value:

- Common Measure:

- Image Search Terms:

Metric Prefix #9:

- Value:

- Common Measure:

- Image Search Terms:

Metric Prefix #10:

- Value:

- Common Measure:

- Image Search Terms:

Student Activity
TypeWithMe: Famous Scientists

Grade Level: Content Area(s):
Elementary/Intermediate Science (3-8)

On CD-ROM:
FamousScientistsSAS.pdf
FamousScientistsGroupDirections.doc
FamousScientistsList.doc

Lesson Overview:
Students will collaborate with two or three peers to write a summarized biography of a chosen/assigned scientist. For this, they will use TypeWithMe – an online tool that will allow students to see exactly what other students in the team are typing as they type. Students will first research the early life, education, and contributions of their scientists and record their findings on the Student Activity Sheet. Using TypeWithMe, students will then write a grammatically correct summary of the scientist's life. Finally, students will export their collaborative documents, make any necessary adjustments, then turn in or print their work for assessment purposes.

Software or Special Materials/Supplies:
Student Activity Sheet
Web browser (Firefox recommended)
Microsoft Word (optional)

Standards:
NSES K-4 Content Standard E and G
  • Women and men of all ages, backgrounds, and groups engage in a variety of scientific and technological work.
  • Men and women have made a variety of contributions throughout the history of science and technology.
  • Many people choose science as a career and devote their entire lives to studying it. Many people derive great pleasure from doing science.

NSES 5-8 Content Standard G
  • Women and men of various social and ethnic backgrounds--and with diverse interests, talents, qualities, and motivations--engage in the activities of science, engineering, and related fields such as the health professions. Some scientists work in teams, and some work alone, but all communicate extensively with others.
  • Many individuals have contributed to the traditions of science. Studying some of these individuals provides further understanding of scientific inquiry, science as a human endeavor, the nature of science, and the relationships between science and society.

Science TEKS

(Grades 3-8)
3d: The student uses critical thinking, scientific reasoning, and problem solving to make informed decisions and knows the contributions of relevant scientists. The student is expected to relate the impact of research on scientific thought and society, including the history of science and contributions of scientists as related to the content.

Procedures:

Before Computer Work Begins

1. Print the necessary sections of the *User's Guide to TypeWithMe*.
2. Create as many TypeWithMe pads as necessary to accommodate each group of three or four students. For security reasons, it is best to use the "Click to Create a New Document" button which creates an obscure URL for each pad.
3. Write or type the URL for each group on the FamousScientistsGroupDirections.doc document.
4. Decide on the final format of the document to be turned in. Edit *Step Four* of the directions sheet to reflect this. Print the directions, one for each student, making sure the groups contain no more than four students.
5. Prepare a list of websites or other resources from which students can obtain their facts.
6. Divide students into groups of three or four students
7. Distribute the Student Activity Sheet and explain to students that they will be working as a team to write a summary of a famous scientist's biography. You may allow students to select their own scientists or print and cut the scientists cards (FamousScientistsList.pdf) and allow students to draw. Keep in mind that the entire group should research the same scientist.
8. Allow plenty of time for students to gather facts about their chosen/selected scientists. This process may take more than an entire class period.
9. Distribute the Group Directions half-sheets.
10. Allow students ample time to read the directions.
11. Reiterate the TypeWithMe rules with the students, being sure to explain your policy on using the built-in chat. This chat feature can be both very helpful and very distracting.
12. Explain to students how they will save their completed projects and turn them into you – and in which format (ex: Word, PDF, Plain Text).
13. Distribute the *User's Guide to TypeWithMe* to students.

Computer Activities

1. Remind students of the requirements for this project as stated on the Group Directions sheet.
2. Guide students in starting a browser and navigating to the specific URL assigned to them.
3. You, as the teacher, should be a member of each TypeWithMe pad to monitor the session.
4. Direct students in editing/entering their names and colors on the open pad.
5. If necessary, show students the basic tools of TypeWithMe, including how to add text and how to save the revisions of their projects.
6. Allow time for students to work.
7. When the first group is finished, demonstrate how to export the TypeWithMe text into the chosen format.
8. Lead students in saving their work and turning in their files or printing their text.

Name: _____   Date: _____

TypeWithMe: Famous Scientists Student Activity Sheet

You and two or three partners will be collaborating to write a summary of the life and contributions of a famous scientist. Using the Internet and/or other resources provided by your teacher, research the following four aspects of the scientist's life. Write at least two statements in each category about your scientist. The more you learn about your scientist, the better your team's collaborative report will be. Be sure to list the sources of your information at the bottom.

Name of Scientist:

Early Life:	Education & Family:	Contributions:

Sources:

Group Members: _____

For today's activity, you will be collaborating with your peers to write a summarized biography of your chosen/assigned scientist. For this, you will use an online tool called TypeWithMe. This will let you see exactly what other students in your team are typing as they type. The rules of using this tool in class are as follows:

TypeWith.me

- Upon entering the TypeWithMe pad, edit your name as instructed by the teacher.
- Each person in the team must have a different color.
- Talking to one another verbally is prohibited.
- You may use the chat feature on the page only with the teacher's permission.
- Everything you write must be appropriate and on-task.
- Avoid typing over your peers – work on different sections of the document at the same time.

Assignment:

1. Access your group's TypeWithMe pad at: http://www.typewith.me/_____

2. Add the names of both group members at the top of the TypeWithMe pad.

3. Use your student activity sheet as a guide to write your summary. You should write a grammatically correct paragraphs.

4. Upon completion, export the TypeWithMe as a Word document. You may make additional edits if necessary. Save the Word document with your name in the file name and turn it in as instructed.

Group Members: _____

For today's activity, you will be collaborating with your peers to write a summarized biography of your chosen/assigned scientist. For this, you will use an online tool called TypeWithMe. This will let you see exactly what other students in your team are typing as they type. The rules of using this tool in class are as follows:

TypeWith.me

- Upon entering the TypeWithMe pad, edit your name as instructed by the teacher.
- Each person in the team must have a different color.
- Talking to one another verbally is prohibited.
- You may use the chat feature on the page only with the teacher's permission.
- Everything you write must be appropriate and on-task.
- Avoid typing over your peers – work on different sections of the document at the same time.

Assignment:

1. Access your group's TypeWithMe pad at: http://www.typewith.me/_____

2. Add the names of both group members at the top of the TypeWithMe pad.

3. Use your student activity sheet as a guide to write your summary. You should write grammatically correct paragraphs.

4. Upon completion, export the TypeWithMe as a Word document. You may make additional edits if necessary. Save the Word document with your name in the file name and turn it in as instructed.

Student Activity
Scrapblog: Science Fair Project

Grade Level: Content Area(s):
Intermediate Science (5-8)

On CD-ROM:
ScienceFairSAS.pdf
ScienceFairSample.URL (shortcut to completed example – available only online)

Lesson Overview:
Students will use Scrapblog to create an online scrapbook, using photographs and text synchronized to a music track to illustrate their science fair project. Students should use the photographs of their projects that they have taken. Students will use these images and add text to explain the sections of a science fair project. Students will then add other embellishments to their Scrapblog such as stickers, frames, and music from the built-in Scrapblog library. Finally, students will share their completed Scrapblog with others by embedding the video into an available website, or posting the link for others.

Software or Special Materials/Supplies:
Student Activity Sheet
Flash-enabled web browser (Firefox recommended)
Photographs of their project

Standards:
NSES 5-8 Content Standards A, E & G
- With practice, students should become competent at communicating experimental methods, following instructions, describing observations, summarizing the results of other groups, and telling other students about investigations and explanations.
- Scientific explanations emphasize evidence, have logically consistent arguments, and use scientific principles, models, and theories.
- Technology used to gather data enhances accuracy and allows scientists to analyze and quantify results of investigations.
- Scientists formulate and test their explanations of nature using observation, experiments, and theoretical and mathematical models.
- Students should review and describe any completed piece of work and identify the stages of problem identification, solution design, implementation, and evaluation.

Science TEKS

(Grades 3-8)
2a-g: The student uses scientific methods during laboratory and outdoor investigations. The student is expected to:
   a. describe, plan, and implement simple experimental investigations testing one variable.
   b. ask well-defined questions, formulate testable hypotheses, and select and use appropriate equipment and technology.
   c. collect information by detailed observations and accurate measuring.
   d. analyze and interpret information to construct reasonable explanations from direct (observable) and indirect (inferred) evidence.
   e. demonstrate that repeated investigations may increase the reliability of results.
   f. communicate valid conclusions in both written and verbal forms.
   g. construct appropriate simple graphs, tables, maps, and charts using technology, including computers, to organize, examine and evaluate information.

Procedures:
This lesson should be carried out after the student has created a science fair project and is intended to reinforce concepts that have already been introduced.

Before Computer Work Begins

1. If you have not already done so, create either a generic account at Scrapblog for all the students to log into, or make arrangements to create individual accounts for students. (See *User's Guide to Scrapblog* for more information.)
2. Distribute the Student Activity Sheets for students to plan their Scrapblogs. You may want to consider assigning the Student Activity Sheet for homework or completing them in class the day prior to creating the Scrapblog. Allow students plenty of time to complete the activity sheet.
3. Assist students with placing their photographs in a location where they can be accessed by Scrapblog.
4. If students are sharing a generic login, then images can also be preloaded into the photo library. This will be especially beneficial for younger students.
5. Decide how the final Scrapblogs will be shared and accessed. Students will provide a link to the online video, or embed the video into another website (like a blog or wiki).
6. Print the necessary sections of the *User's Guide to Scrapblog*.

Computer Activities

1. Remind students of the requirements for this project as stated on the Student Activity Sheet.
   - Title/Credits Slide
   - Introduction and Purpose
   - Hypothesis or Question
   - Materials
   - Method
   - Data
   - Results
   - Conclusion
   - References
2. Guide students to http://www.scrapblog.com.
3. Have students log on with accounts as determined prior to class.
4. Lead students in beginning a new project, referring to the User's Guide as needed.
5. Demonstrate how to upload the necessary images and use them in the Scrapblog.
6. Demonstrate how to apply text, stickers and other embellishments.
7. Guide students in adding new slides, and how to reorder slides as needed.
8. Allow students time to complete the slides according to the sketches on their Student Activity Sheet.
9. Guide students in selecting appropriate music and transitions.
10. Lead students in saving and publishing the Scrapblog, including specific instructions on how to share their projects for assessment purposes.

Name: _____ Date: _____

Science Fair Project

Now that you have completed your science fair project, it's time to create your display using Scrapblog. Use the photographs you have taken of your project to illustrate your work. Use text to carefully explain each section of your project. Be sure to include the citations of the resources you used. Use as many slides as you need to complete your project.

Use this sheet as a guide to help plan for your project.
In each box, fill in the appropriate information.

Section 1: Title

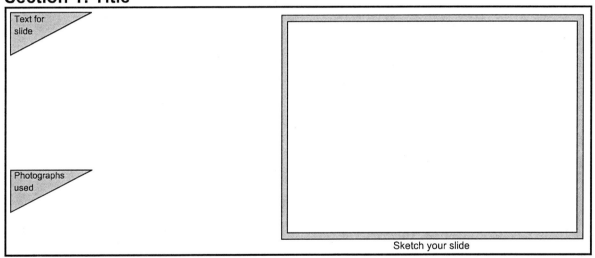

Text for slide

Photographs used

Sketch your slide

Section 2: Introduction and Purpose

Text for slide

Photographs used

Sketch your slide

Section 2: Introduction and Purpose (continued)

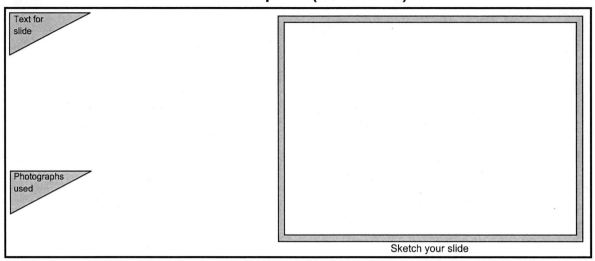

Section 3: Hypothesis or Question

Section 4: Materials

Section 5: Method

Section 5: Method (continued)

Section 6: Data

Section 7: Results

Section 8: Conclusion

Section 9: References

use as needed

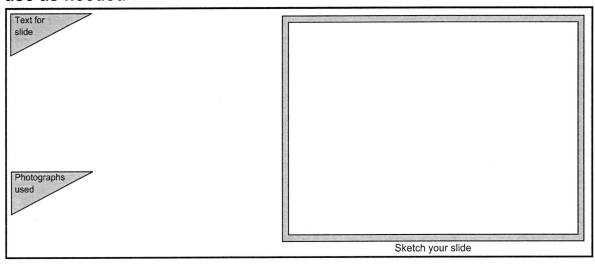

use as needed

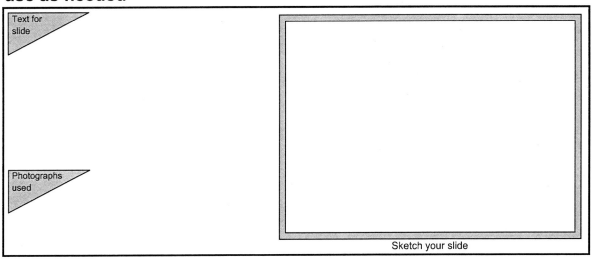

use as needed

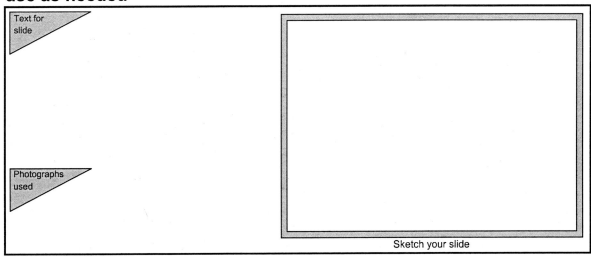

Student Activity
TinyPaste: Cellular Organelles

Grade Level: Content Area(s):
Intermediate Science (5-8)

On CD-ROM:
OrganellesSAS.pdf
OrganellesSample.URL (shortcut to completed example – available only online)

Lesson Overview:
Students will use TinyPaste to create a textbin of parts of a plant cell. Students will research the role of each part of a plant cell, and will use a Student Activity Sheet to record this information. Students will also find an online image to illustrate the role of the organelle, and will use the image and text to create a TinyPaste. Students can preview their TinyPaste and make revisions until they are satisfied with the final result. Students then can record the URL of their TinyPaste.

Software or Special Materials/Supplies:
Student Activity Sheet
Flash-enabled web browser (Firefox recommended)

Standards:
NSES 5-8 Content Standard C
- Living systems at all levels of organization demonstrate the complementary nature of structure and function. Important levels of organization for structure and function include cells...
- All organisms are composed of cells—the fundamental unit of life. Most organisms are single cells; other organisms, including humans, are multicellular. Cells carry on the many functions needed to sustain life.
- Specialized cells perform specialized functions in multicellular organisms. Groups of specialized cells cooperate to form a tissue, such as a muscle. Different tissues are in turn grouped together to form larger functional units, called organs. Each type of cell, tissue, and organ has a distinct structure and set of functions that serve the organism as a whole.

Science TEKS

(Grades 3-8)
7.12d-f: The student knows that living systems at all levels of organization demonstrate the complementary nature of structure and function. The student is expected to:
- d. differentiate between structure and function in plant and animal cell organelles, including cell membrane, cell wall, nucleus, cytoplasm, mitochondrion, chloroplast, and vacuole.
- e. compare the functions of a cell to the functions of organisms such as waste removal.
- f. recognize that according to cell theory all organisms are composed of cells and cells carry on similar functions such as extracting energy from food to sustain life.

Procedures:

This lesson should follow a brief introduction of cellular organelles and is intended to reinforce concepts that have already been introduced.

Before Computer Work Begins

1. Distribute the Student Activity Sheets for students to plan their TinyPaste. You may want to consider assigning the Student Activity Sheet for homework or completing them in class the day prior to creating the TinyPaste. Allow students plenty of time to complete the activity sheet.
2. Students will need online images to complete this activity. Decide where they will get these images. (See the *User's Guide to TinyPaste.*)
3. Print the necessary sections of the *User's Guide to TinyPaste.*

Computer Activities

1. Remind students of the requirements for this project as stated on the Student Activity Sheet.
2. Guide students to http://www.tinypaste.com.
3. Lead students in beginning a new project, referring to the User's Guide as needed.
4. Demonstrate how to create a TinyPaste including adding an image, increasing text size to make a title, and adding text to describe the insect body part.
5. Lead students in saving and publishing the TinyPaste, including recording the URL.

Name: _____ Date: _____

CELLULAR ORGANELLES

http://tinypaste.com

Organelle	Role of the organism	How it can be represented	TinyPaste address
cell membrane	a thick, rigid semi-permeable membrane that surrounds a plant cell. This layer of cellulose fiber gives the cell most of its support and structure.	chicken wire	http://tinypaste.com/0f70b
cell wall			
chloroplasts			
chromosomes			
endoplasmic reticulum			

golgi body			
lysosome			
mitochrondria			
nucleus			
ribosomes			
vacuoles			

Student Activity
TypeWithMe: Steps of Mitosis

Grade Level: Content Area(s):
Intermediate Science (7-8)

On CD-ROM:
MitosisSAS.pdf
MitosisGroupDirections.doc
Mitosis-sample.pdf

Lesson Overview:
Students will collaborate with a partner to write a summary of what happens during mitosis. For this, they will use TypeWithMe – an online tool that will allow students to see exactly what other students in the team are typing as they type. Students will first research the steps of mitosis and record their findings on the Student Activity Sheet, along with illustrations. Using TypeWithMe, students will then write a grammatically correct summary of the entire mitotic process. Finally, students will export their collaborative documents, make any necessary adjustments, then turn in or print their work for assessment purposes.

Software or Special Materials/Supplies:
Student Activity Sheet
Web browser (Firefox recommended)
Microsoft Word (optional)

Standards:
NSES 5-8 Content Standard C
  • Reproduction is a characteristic of all living systems; because no individual organism lives forever, reproduction is essential to the continuation of every species. Some organisms reproduce asexually. Other organisms reproduce sexually.
  • Hereditary information is contained in genes, located in the chromosomes of each cell. Each gene carries a single unit of information. An inherited trait of an individual can be determined by one or by many genes, and a single gene can influence more than one trait. A human cell contains many thousands of different genes.

Science TEKS

7.6b: The student knows that living systems at all levels of organization demonstrate the complementary nature of structure and function. They student is expected to recognize that according to cell theory all organisms are composted of cells and cells carry on similar functions such as extracting energy from food to sustain life.

7.14c: The student knows that reproduction is a characteristic of living organisms and that the instructions for traits are governed in the genetic material. The student is expected to recognize that inherited traits of individuals are governed in the genetic material found in the genes within chromosomes in the nucleus.

Procedures:
This lesson should follow an introduction to mitosis and is intended as a reinforcement activity.

Before Computer Work Begins

1. Print the necessary sections of the *User's Guide to TypeWithMe*.
2. Create as many TypeWithMe pads as necessary to accommodate each pair of students. For security reasons, it is best to use the "Click to Create a New Document" button which creates an obscure URL for each pad.
3. Write or type the URL for each group on the MitosisGroupDirections.doc document.
4. Decide on the final format of the document to be turned in. Edit *Step Four* of the directions sheet to reflect this. Print the directions one for each student, making sure the groups contain no more than two students.
5. Prepare a list of websites or other resources from which students can obtain their facts.
6. Divide students into pairs.
7. Distribute the Student Activity Sheet and explain to students that they will be working as a team to write a summary of the phases of Mitosis (including the Interphase of the cell cycle).
8. Allow plenty of time for students to gather facts about the mitosis phases. This process may take more than an entire class period.
9. Distribute the Group Directions half-sheets.
10. Allow students ample time to read the directions.
11. Reiterate the TypeWithMe rules with the students, being sure to explain your policy on using the built-in chat. This chat feature can be both very helpful and very distracting.
12. Explain to students how they will save their completed projects and turn them into you – and in which format (ex: Word, PDF, Plain Text).
13. Distribute the *User's Guide to TypeWithMe* to students.

Computer Activities

1. Remind students of the requirements for this project as stated on the Group Directions sheet.
2. Guide students in starting a browser and navigating to the specific URL assigned to them.
3. You, as the teacher, should be a member of each TypeWithMe pad to monitor the session.
4. Direct students in editing/entering their names and colors on the open pad.
5. If necessary, show students the basic tools of TypeWithMe, including how to add text and how to save the revisions of their projects.
6. Allow time for students to work.
7. When the first group is finished, demonstrate how to export the TypeWithMe text into the chosen format.
8. Lead students in saving their work and turning in their files or printing their text.

Name: _____   Date: _____

TypeWithMe: Mitosis Student Activity Sheet

You and a partner will collaborate to explain what happens during each stage of cellular mitosis. Using the Internet and/or other resources provided by your teacher, fill in this diagram to help organize your thoughts. List the name of the phase, then explain what happens during that phase. Make a sketch of each step to help guide your writing later. Though "Interphase" is not really part of mitosis, it is included here and should be included in your final writing. Be sure to list the sources of your information at the bottom of this page.

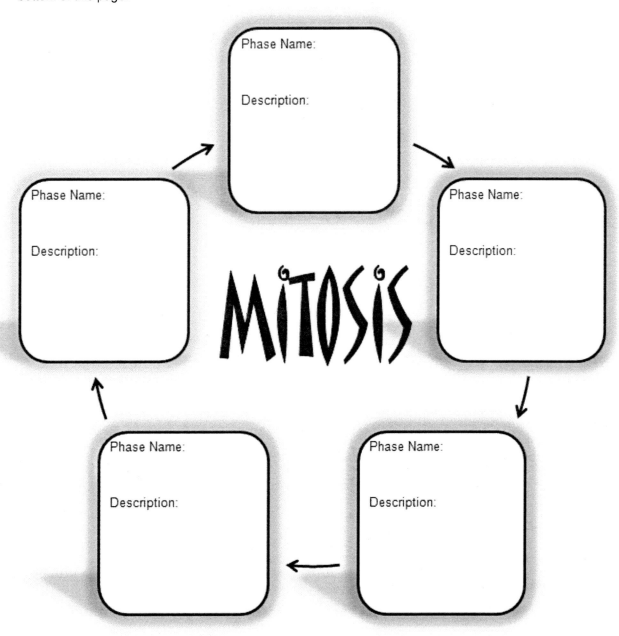

Sources:

Group Members: _____

For today's activity, you will be collaborating with your peers to write a summarized biography of your chosen/assigned scientist. For this, you will use an online tool called TypeWithMe. This will let you see exactly what other students in your team are typing as they type. The rules of using this tool in class are as follows:

TypeWith.me

- Upon entering the TypeWithMe pad, edit your name as instructed by the teacher.
- Each person in the team must have a different color.
- Talking to one another verbally is prohibited.
- You may use the chat feature on the page only with the teacher's permission.
- Everything you write must be appropriate and on-task.
- Avoid typing over your peers – work on different sections of the document at the same time.

Assignment:

1. Access your group's TypeWithMe pad at: http://www.typewith.me/_____

2. Add the names of both group members at the top of the TypeWithMe pad.

3. Use your student activity sheet as a guide to write your summary. You should write a grammatically correct paragraph for each of the five phases.

4. Upon completion, export the TypeWithMe as a Word document. You may make additional edits if necessary. Save the Word document with your name in the file name and turn it in as instructed.

Group Members: _____

For today's activity, you will be collaborating with your peers to write a summarized biography of your chosen/assigned scientist. For this, you will use an online tool called TypeWithMe. This will let you see exactly what other students in your team are typing as they type. The rules of using this tool in class are as follows:

TypeWith.me

- Upon entering the TypeWithMe pad, edit your name as instructed by the teacher.
- Each person in the team must have a different color.
- Talking to one another verbally is prohibited.
- You may use the chat feature on the page only with the teacher's permission.
- Everything you write must be appropriate and on-task.
- Avoid typing over your peers – work on different sections of the document at the same time.

Assignment:

1. Access your group's TypeWithMe pad at: http://www.typewith.me/_____

2. Add the names of both group members at the top of the TypeWithMe pad.

3. Use your student activity sheet as a guide to write your summary. You should write a grammatically correct paragraph for each of the five phases.

4. Upon completion, export the TypeWithMe as a Word document. You may make additional edits if necessary. Save the Word document with your name in the file name and turn it in as instructed.

Student Activity

BigHugeLabs Trading Cards: Digestive Process

Grade Level: Content Area(s):
Intermediate Science (5-8)

On CD-ROM:
DigestionSAS.pdf
DigestionSample.pdf
Digestion Images (folder)
Digestion Sample Cards (folder)

Lesson Overview:
Students will use the BigHugeLabs Trading Card generator to create a series of collectible cards, each having an image, title, and descriptive text to illustrate and explain the steps of digestion. Students may either gather images from the Internet or other sources, or may use the ones supplied on the CD (especially if time is limited). Finally, students will save and share their completed trading cards in print format or by displaying them within a slideshow or document.

Software or Special Materials/Supplies:
Student Activity Sheet
Javascript-enabled web browser (Firefox recommended)
Resources for obtaining images (optional)

Standards:
NSES 5-8 Content Standard C
- The human organism has systems for digestion, respiration, reproduction, circulation, excretion, movement, control, and coordination, and for protection from disease. These systems interact with one another.
- Specialized cells perform specialized functions in multicellular organisms. Groups of specialized cells cooperate to form a tissue, such as a muscle. Different tissues are in turn grouped together to form larger functional units, called organs. Each type of cell, tissue, and organ has a distinct structure and set of functions that serve the organism as a whole.

Science TEKS

7.6b: The student knows that matter has physical and chemical properties and can undergo physical and chemical changes. The student is expected to distinguish between physical and chemical changes in matter in the digestive system.

7.12b: The student knows that living systems at all levels of organization demonstrate the complementary nature of structure and function. The student is expected to identify the main functions of the systems of the human organism, including the circulatory, respiratory, skeletal, muscular, digestive, excretory, reproductive, integumentary, nervous, and endocrine systems.

Procedures:
This lesson should follow an introduction to digestion and is intended for reinforcement.

Before Computer Work Begins

1. To introduce this activity, show the completed sample (DigestionSample.pdf on CD).
2. Distribute the Student Activity Sheet and explain to students that they must create trading cards to explain what happens at each phase of the digestive process.
3. Gather a list of resources that students may use to obtain information.
4. You may want to consider assigning the Student Activity Sheet for homework or completing it in class the day prior to creating the trading cards.
5. Decide whether students will be responsible for obtaining their own images or will use the ones provided on the CD. Images that represent each of the digestive phases may be difficult to find. Keep in mind that students may choose to find images that merely represent what happens at each phase (ex: sponge for absorption in the small intestine, etc.). Images of the digestive organs that are in the public domain and free to use may be found on sites such as Wikipedia.org. If students are using the images provided on the CD, upload these files to a shared network location, or distribute the files according to standard procedures.
6. Decide how the final trading cards will be shared and accessed. Students will either print their cards or embed the image files into a slideshow, such as PowerPoint, or into a word processing document.
7. Print the necessary sections of the *User's Guide to BigHugeLabs Trading Cards*.

Computer Activities

1. Remind students of the requirements for each card in this project as stated on the Student Activity Sheet.
    *   Title: Name of the organ/part of the body
    *   An image representing the part
    *   Description of what takes place at the location
    *   Citations for the information and image source
2. Guide students in obtaining images, either from the ones supplied on the CD (which have been placed in a student-accessible location) or from various image websites (see the introductory section of this book for a list of some sites).
3. Guide students to http://bighugelabs.com/deck.php.
4. Lead students in beginning a new project, referring to the User's Guide as needed.
5. Demonstrate how to upload the image.
6. Walk students through the process of selecting cropping options and a background color.
7. Using the Student Activity Sheet as a guide, allow students time to enter the necessary text in the appropriate fields.
8. Guide students in selecting symbols to add to the card (if desired).
9. Demonstrate how to create the card and save or copy it to an appropriate location.
10. Once the collection of cards has been created and saved, give students specific instructions for printing or inserting into a document.

Name: _____   Date: _____

BigHugeLabs Trading Cards: The Digestive Process

For this activity, you will use the BigHugeLabs Trading Card generator to create **six** cards describing each stage of the digestive process. You must include the following on each card:
- Title: Name of the organ/part of the body
- An image representing the part
- Description of what takes place at this location
- Citations for your information and image source

You will save the trading card images so that they can either be printed or embedded into another application such as PowerPoint or Microsoft Word according to your teacher's directions.

Use this sheet as a guide to help plan for your project. In each box, fill in the appropriate information.

Mouth	Description:	Image Search Terms:

Esophagus	Description:	Image Search Terms:

Stomach	Description:	Image Search Terms:

Small Intestine	Description:	Image Search Terms:

Pancreas	Description:	Image Search Terms:

Large Intestine	Description:	Image Search Terms:

Student Activity
Wordle: Acquired and Inherited Traits

Grade Level: Content Area(s):
Intermediate Science (5-8)

On CD-ROM:
Acquired-InheritedSAS.pdf
AcquiredTraits.jpg
InheritedTraits.jpg

Lesson Overview:
Students will use Wordle to create a word cloud using words
and phrases that identify acquired and inherited traits. Students will
brainstorm ideas for each type of traits and will use a Student Activity Sheet to record these ideas.
Students will then create their Wordle and will refine the results until they are satisfied with the final result.
Students will then either print or create a screen capture of the Wordle.

Software or Special Materials/Supplies:
Student Activity Sheet
Flash-enabled web browser (Firefox recommended)

Standards:
NSES 5-8 Content Standard C
- Every organism requires a set of instructions for specifying its traits. Heredity is the passage of these instructions from one generation to another.
- The characteristics of an organism can be described in terms of a combination of traits. Some traits are inherited and others result from interactions with the environment.

Science TEKS

5.10b: The student knows that organisms undergo similar life processes and have structures that help them survive within their environments. The student is expected to differentiate between inherited traits of plants and animals such as spines on a cactus or shape of a beak and learned behaviors such as an animal learning tricks or a child riding a bicycle.

7.14c: The student knows that reproduction is a characteristic of living organisms and that the instructions for traits are governed in the genetic material. The student is expected to recognize that inherited traits of individuals are governed in the genetic material found in the genes within chromosomes in the nucleus.

Procedures:
This lesson should follow a brief introduction of acquired and inherited traits and is intended to reinforce concepts that have already been introduced.

Before Computer Work Begins

1. Have students use the Acquired-Inherited Student Activity Sheet to brainstorm words and phrases to describe each of the types of traits.
2. Print the necessary sections of the *User's Guide to Wordle*.

Computer Activities

1. Remind students of the requirements for this project as stated on the Student Activity Sheet.
2. Guide students to http://www.wordle.net/create.
3. Lead students in beginning a new project, referring to the User's Guide as needed.
4. Demonstrate how to insert the tilde (~) character between words in a phrase.
5. Demonstrate how to adjust size of words in the Wordle by increasing the number of times the word is entered into the list.
6. Students will click **Go** to create the Wordle and then will revise the Wordle until a pleasing configuration is found.
7. Students will then print their Wordle or use a screen capture to save their Wordle as a .jpg or another format.

Name: _____ Date: _____

INHERITED VS. ACQUIRED TRAITS

Everybody has certain traits that are inherited from their family, and other traits that are acquired through activities in their lives. List some of the traits below, and then create two Wordles for the Inherited Traits and Acquired Traits. Remember, when entering in phrases they need a tilde (~) between each word to keep them together. For example, **hair color and texture** would need to be typed in as **hair~color~and~texture**. Type the name of the title in several times so it is larger than the traits.

www.wordle.net/create

ACQUIRED TRAITS

INHERITED TRAITS

Student Activity
Mixbook: The Five Senses

Grade Level: Content Area(s):
Elementary Science (3-5)

On CD-ROM:
FiveSensesSAS.pdf
FiveSensesSample.URL (shortcut to completed example – available only online)
Five Senses Images (folder)

Lesson Overview:
Students will use Mixbook to create an online animated book using still images, titles, example sentences, and stickers to illustrate and describe how the five human senses are used. Students may either gather images from the Internet or other sources, or may use the ones supplied on the CD (especially if time is limited). Using the storyboard as a guide, students will select appropriate layouts and backgrounds, then enter graphics and text onto the pre-formatted page. Finally, students will share their completed Mixbooks either by embedding the animated book into an available website or by posting the link for others.

Software or Special Materials/Supplies:
Student Activity Sheet
Mixbook Storyboard
Flash-enabled web browser (Firefox recommended)
Resources for obtaining images (optional)

Standards:
NSES 5-8 Content Standard G
- Scientists formulate and test their explanations of nature using observation, experiments, and theoretical and mathematical models. Although all scientific ideas are tentative and subject to change and improvement in principle, for most major ideas in science, there is much experimental and observational confirmation. Those ideas are not likely to change greatly in the future. Scientists do and have changed their ideas about nature when they encounter new experimental evidence that does not match their existing explanations.

Science TEKS

(Grades 3-4)
3a: The student knows that information, critical thinking, scientific problem solving, and the contributions of scientists are used in making decisions. The student is expected to in all fields of science, analyze, evaluate, and critique scientific explanations by using empirical evidence, logical reasoning, and experimental and observational testing, including examining all sides of scientific evidence of those scientific explanations, so as to encourage critical thinking by the student.

Procedures:
This lesson can either follow a lesson on the five senses or be used as an introductory lesson as long as students are given the proper resources for locating the information.

Before Computer Work Begins

1. To introduce this activity, show the completed sample (FiveSensesSample.URL on CD).
2. Distribute the Student Activity Sheet and explain to students that they must illustrate and explain how the five human senses are used.
3. Distribute the blank Mixbook Storyboard sheets for students to plan their books. You may want to consider assigning both the Student Activity Sheet and Mixbook Storyboard for homework or completing them in class the day prior to creating the Mixbook.
4. Decide whether students will be responsible for obtaining their own images or will use the ones provided on the CD. If students are using the provided images, upload these files to a shared network location or distribute the files according to standard procedures.
5. Decide how the final Mixbooks will be shared and accessed. Students will either provide a link to the online book, or embed the book as a widget into another website (like a blog or wiki).
6. Print the necessary sections of the *User's Guide to Mixbook*.

Computer Activities

1. Remind students of the requirements for this project as stated on the Student Activity Sheet.
   - Title & Credits pages
   - 1-page spread for each of the senses with the following text:
     - Name of the sense
     - Explanation of how we use the sense
   - At least two images and example sentences demonstrating the use of each sense
2. Guide students in obtaining images, either from the ones supplied on the CD (which have been placed in a student-accessible location) or from various image websites (see the introductory section of this book for a list of some sites).
3. Guide students to http://www.mixbook.com.
4. If students have no Mixbook accounts, follow the account sign-up procedures outlined in the *User's Guide to Mixbook*.
5. Lead students in beginning a new project, referring to the User's Guide as needed.
6. Demonstrate how to upload the necessary images.
7. Walk students through the process of selecting and editing a background.
8. Using the storyboard as a guide, allow students time to add or remove pages as needed. Once the background is selected for either the cover or the first page, it may be best to duplicate that page rather than having to re-create the same background on each page.
9. Guide students in selecting appropriate layouts by practicing with page one.
10. Review, if necessary, how students can add photos or stickers to page one and make needed edits.
11. Demonstrate how to add and edit text elements on page one.
12. Make yourself available as students continue working at their own pace.
13. Lead students in publishing the book, including specific instructions on how to share their projects by linking or embedding.

Name: _____   Date: _____

Mixbook: The Five Senses

For this activity, you will create a Mixbook animated photo album with images and text to explain each of the five senses we use to observe the world around us. You must include the following in your Mixbook:
- Title & Credits pages
- 1-page spread for each of the senses with the following text:
  - Name of sense
  - Explanation of how we use the sense
- At least two images and example sentences demonstrating the use of each sense
  - Ex: Sight: "The yellow flower is beautiful."

Use this sheet as a guide to help plan for your project. In each box, fill in the appropriate information.

Seeing

Example Sentences demonstrating the use of the sense:

Image Search Terms:

Smelling

Example Sentences demonstrating the use of the sense:

Image Search Terms:

Hearing

Example Sentences demonstrating the use of the sense:

Image Search Terms:

Tasting

Example Sentences demonstrating the use of the sense:

Image Search Terms:

Feeling

Example Sentences demonstrating the use of the sense:

Image Search Terms:

Student Activity
Animoto Video: Characteristics of Living Things

Grade Level: Content Area(s):
Elementary/Intermediate Science (3-8)

On CD-ROM:
LivingThingsSAS.pdf
LivingThingsSample.mp4
Living Things Images (folder)
Living Things Title Slides (folder)

Lesson Overview:
Students will use Animoto to create a video using still images and title slides synchronized to a music track to illustrate and explain selected characteristics shared by all living things. Students may either gather images from the Internet or other sources, or may use the ones supplied on the CD (especially if time is limited). In addition, students will add titles to introduce and explain each of the characteristics. These titles may be added from within Animoto, or may be created using PowerPoint or other similar applications. The music soundtrack may be uploaded by students or may be chosen from Animoto's music library (recommended). Finally, students will share their completed videos either by downloading the file, embedding the video into an available website, or posting the link for others.

Software or Special Materials/Supplies:
Student Activity Sheet
Animoto Storyboard
Flash-enabled web browser (Firefox recommended)
PowerPoint (optional)
Resources for obtaining images (optional)

Standards:
NSES 5-8 Content Standard C
- Living systems at all levels of organization demonstrate the complementary nature of structure and function. Important levels of organization for structure and function include cells, organs, tissues, organ systems, whole organisms, and ecosystems.
- Reproduction is a characteristic of all living systems; because no individual organism lives forever, reproduction is essential to the continuation of every species. Some organisms reproduce asexually. Other organisms reproduce sexually.
- All organisms must be able to obtain and use resources, grow, reproduce, and maintain stable internal conditions while living in a constantly changing external environment.
- Regulation of an organism's internal environment involves sensing the internal environment and changing physiological activities to keep conditions within the range required to survive.

Science TEKS

(Grades 3-5)
9a: The student knows that organisms have characteristics that help them survive and can describe patterns, cycles, systems, and relationships within the environments. The student is expected to observe and describe the physical characteristics of environments and how they support populations and communities within an ecosystem.

10a-b: The student knows that organisms undergo similar life processes and have structures that help them survive within their environments. The student is expected to:
   a. explore how structures and functions of plants and animals allow them to survive in a particular environment.
   b. explore that some characteristics of organisms are inherited such as the number of limbs on an animal or flower color and recognize that some behaviors are learned in response to living in a certain environment such as animals using tools to get food.

7.12a-b: The student knows that living systems at all levels of organization demonstrate the complementary nature of structure and function. The student is expected to:
   a. investigate and explain how internal structures of organisms have adaptations that allow specific functions such as gills in fish, hollow bones in birds, or xylem in plants.
   b. identify the main functions of the systems of the human organism, including the circulatory, respiratory, skeletal, muscular, digestive, excretory, reproductive, integumentary, nervous, and endocrine systems.

Procedures:
This lesson should follow a brief introduction of the characteristics shared by all living things and is intended for reinforcement.

Before Computer Work Begins

1. If you have not already done so, apply for an educator account at http://www.animoto.com to obtain the registration code for students. This must be done at least a week before the computer activity begins since the application approval process may take several days.
2. To introduce this activity, show the completed Living Things Animoto video (LivingThingsSample.mp4).
3. Distribute the Student Activity Sheet and explain to students that they must illustrate and explain the characteristics of living things in this project. Because different curricula classify these differently, explain to students how many they must include according to your curriculum.
4. Distribute the blank Animoto Storyboard sheets for students to plan their videos. You may want to consider assigning both the Student Activity Sheet and Animoto Storyboard for homework or completing them in class the day prior to creating the Animoto video.
5. Decide whether students will be responsible for obtaining their own images or will use the ones provided on the CD. If students are using the provided images, upload these files to a shared network location or distribute the files according to standard procedures.
6. Decide whether students will be responsible for creating their own title/description slides or will use the ones provided on the CD. If students are using the provided text slides, upload these files to a shared network location or distribute the files according to standard procedures.
7. Decide how the final Animoto videos will be shared and accessed. Students will either download and turn in the video file, provide a link to the online video, or embed the video into another website (like a blog or wiki).
8. Print the necessary sections of the *User's Guide to Animoto*.

Computer Activities

1. Remind students of the requirements for this project as stated on the Student Activity Sheet.
   - Title & Credits Slides
   - Title slide for each characteristic
   - Brief description slide for each characteristic
   - At least two images representing each characteristic
2. Guide students in obtaining images, either from the ones supplied on the CD (which have been placed in a student-accessible location) or from various image websites (see the introductory section of this book for a list of some sites).
3. Direct students in creating their title/description slides. Limited title slides can be created within Animoto. However, description slides will need to be created using PowerPoint (or another application). Students may use the provided text slides (.jpg files) or edit the PowerPoint file to create their own.
4. Guide students to http://www.animoto.com.
5. If students have no Animoto accounts, follow the account sign-up procedures outlined in the *User's Guide to Animoto*.
6. Lead students in beginning a new full-length project, referring to the User's Guide as needed.
7. Demonstrate how to upload the necessary images, including any title/description slides (in .jpg format).
8. Allow students time to re-arrange and spotlight images according to their storyboards. If necessary, show students the process of adding title slides from within Animoto.
9. Guide students in selecting appropriate music.
10. Lead students in finalizing the video, including specific instructions on how to share their projects.

Name: _____ Date: _____

Animoto: Characteristics of Living Things Student Activity Sheet

For this activity, you will create a video using still images and text to show your understanding of the characteristics shared by all living things. You must include the following in your Animoto video:

- Title & Credits Slides
- Title slide for each characteristic
- Brief description slide for each characteristic
- At least two images representing each characteristic

Use this sheet as a guide to help plan for your project. In each box, fill in the appropriate information. Even experts cannot agree on how many distinct characteristics are shared by all living things. Your teacher may present fewer characteristics than there are boxes listed here.

Characteristic: Description:

Characteristic: Description:

Characteristic: Description:

Characteristic:

Description:

Characteristic:

Description:

Characteristic:

Description:

Characteristic:

Description:

Characteristic:

Description:

Student Activity
Wordle: Five Kingdoms

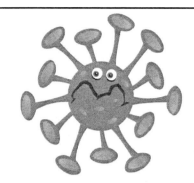

Grade Level: Content Area(s):
Intermediate Science (5-8)

On CD-ROM:
5KingdomsSAS.pdf
MoneraSample.jpg
ProtozoaSample.jpg
FungiSample.jpg
PlantSample.jpg
AnimalSample.jpg

Lesson Overview:
Students will use Wordle to create a word cloud using words and phrases associated with the five kingdoms. Students will brainstorm ideas for each of the kingdoms and will use a Student Activity Sheet to record these ideas. Students will then create their Wordle and will refine the results until they are satisfied with the final result. Students will then either print or create a screen capture of the Wordle.

Software or Special Materials/Supplies:
Student Activity Sheet
Flash-enabled web browser (Firefox recommended)

Standards:
NSES 5-8 Content Standard C
- Living systems at all levels of organization demonstrate the complementary nature of structure and function. Important levels of organization for structure and function include cells…
- All organisms are composed of cells--the fundamental unit of life. Most organisms are single cells; other organisms, including humans, are multicellular. Cells carry on the many functions needed to sustain life.
- Specialized cells perform specialized functions in multicellular organisms. Groups of specialized cells cooperate to form a tissue, such as a muscle. Different tissues are in turn grouped together to form larger functional units, called organs. Each type of cell, tissue, and organ has a distinct structure and set of functions that serve the organism as a whole.

Science TEKS

6.12d: The student knows all organisms are classified into Domains and Kingdoms. Organisms within these taxonomic groups share similar characteristics which allow them to interact with the living and nonliving parts of their ecosystem. The student is expected to identify the basic characteristics of organisms, including prokaryotic or eukaryotic, unicellular or multicellular, autotrophic or heterotrophic, and mode of reproduction, that further classify them in the currently recognized Kingdoms.

7.12a: The student knows that living systems at all levels of organization demonstrate the complementary nature of structure and function. The student is expected to investigate and explain how internal structures of organisms have adaptations that allow specific functions such as gills in fish, hollow bones in birds, or xylem in plants.

Procedures:
This lesson should follow a brief introduction of the five kingdoms and is intended to reinforce concepts that have already been introduced.

Before Computer Work Begins

1. Have students use the 5Kingdoms Student Activity Sheet to brainstorm words and phrases about each of the kingdoms.
2. Print the necessary sections of the *User's Guide to Wordle*.

Computer Activities

1. Remind students of the requirements for this project as stated on the Student Activity Sheet.
2. Guide students to http://www.wordle.net/create.
3. Lead students in beginning a new project, referring to the User's Guide as needed.
4. Demonstrate how to insert the tilde (~) character between words in a phrase.
5. Demonstrate how to adjust size of words in the Wordle by increasing the number of times the word is entered into the list.
6. Students will click **Go** to create the Wordle and then revise the Wordle until a pleasing configuration is found.
7. Students will then print their Wordle, or will use a screen capture to save their Wordle as a .jpg or another format.

Name: _____ Date: _____

The 5 Kingdoms

For this activity, you will identify traits of each of the 5 kingdoms. List some of the traits below and then create a Wordle for each of the kingdoms. Remember, when entering in phrases they need a tilde (~) between each word to keep them together. For example, **motile and non-motile** would need to be typed in as **motile~and~non-motile**. Type the name of the kingdom in several times so it is larger than the traits.

www.wordle.net/create

Student Activity
TinyPaste: Insects

Grade Level: Content Area(s):
Intermediate Science (5-8)

On CD-ROM:
InsectsSAS.pdf
InsectsSample.URL (shortcut to completed example – available only online)

Lesson Overview:
Students will use TinyPaste to demonstrate knowledge of the parts of an insect body. Students will collect information about insects and will use a Student Activity Sheet to record this information. Students will also find an online image to demonstrate the specified body part, and will use the image and text to create a TinyPaste. Students can preview their TinyPaste and make revisions until they are satisfied with the final result. Students then can record the URL of their TinyPaste.

Software or Special Materials/Supplies:
Student Activity Sheet
Flash-enabled web browser (Firefox recommended)

Standards:
NSES 5-8 Content Standard C
- Living systems at all levels of organization demonstrate the complementary nature of structure and function. Important levels of organization for structure and function include cells, organs, tissues, organ systems, whole organisms, and ecosystems.

Science TEKS

5.10a: The student knows that organisms undergo similar life processes and have structures that help them survive within their environments The student is expected to compare the structures and functions of different species that help them live and survive such as hooves on prairie animals or webbed feet in aquatic animals.

7.11a: The student knows that populations and species demonstrate variation and inherit many of their unique traits through gradual processes over many generations. The student is expected to examine organisms or their structures such as insects or leaves and use dichotomous keys for identification.

7.12c: The student knows that living systems at all levels of organization demonstrate the complementary nature of structure and function. The student is expected to recognize levels of organization in plants and animals, including cells, tissues, organs, organ systems, and organisms.

Procedures:
This lesson should follow a brief introduction of insects and is intended to reinforce concepts that have already been introduced.

Before Computer Work Begins

1. Distribute the Student Activity Sheets for students to plan their TinyPaste. You may want to consider assigning the Student Activity Sheet for homework or completing them in class the day prior to creating the TinyPaste. Allow students plenty of time to complete the activity sheet.
2. Students will need online images to complete this activity. Decide where they will get these images. (See the *User's Guide to TinyPaste*.)
3. Print the necessary sections of the *User's Guide to TinyPaste*.

Computer Activities

1. Remind students of the requirements for this project as stated on the Student Activity Sheet.
2. Guide students to http://www.tinypaste.com.
3. Lead students in beginning a new project, referring to the User's Guide as needed.
4. Demonstrate how to create a TinyPaste including adding an image, increasing text size to make a title, and adding text to describe the insect body part.
5. Lead students in saving and publishing the TinyPaste, including recording the URL.

Name: _____ Date: _____

Insects

There are more species of insects than any other group, but they all have many things in common. Identify the body parts of insects and tell the indentifying characteristics of that part. You will use this information to create a TinyPaste for each body part type, including an image. Use this sheet as a guide to help plan for your project. In each box, fill in the appropriate information.

http://tinypaste.com

Insect Body Part	Description	TinyPaste Address
Head		
Antennae		
Mouth parts		
Thorax		
Wings		
Legs		
Abdomen		

Student Activity
Scrapblog: Butterfly Life Cycle

Grade Level: Content Area(s):
Intermediate Science (5-8)

On CD-ROM:
ButterflyLifeCycleSAS.pdf
Butterfly Life Cycle Images (folder)
ButterflyLifeSample.URL (shortcut to completed example – available only online)

Lesson Overview:
Students will use Scrapblog to create an online scrapbook using photographs and text synchronized to a music track to illustrate the life cycle of a butterfly. Student may either gather images from the Internet or other sources, or may use the ones supplied on the CD (especially if time is limited). Students will use these images and add text to explain the processes of butterfly transformation. Students will then add other embellishments to their Scrapblog such as stickers, frames, and music from the built-in Scrapblog library. Finally, students will share their completed Scrapblog with others by embedding the video into an available website, or posting the link for others.

Software or Special Materials/Supplies:
Student Activity Sheet
Flash-enabled web browser (Firefox recommended)
Resources for obtaining images (optional)

Standards:
NSES 5-8 Content Standard C
  • All organisms must be able to obtain and use resources, grow, reproduce, and maintain
    stable internal conditions while living in a constantly changing external environment.
  • Regulation of an organism's internal environment involves sensing the internal environment
    and changing physiological activities to keep conditions within the range required to survive.

Science TEKS

3.10c: The student knows that organisms undergo similar life processes and have structures that help them survive within their environments. The student is expected to investigate and compare how animals and plants undergo a series of orderly changes in their diverse life cycles such as tomato plants, frogs, and ladybugs.

4.10c: The student knows that organisms undergo similar life processes and have structures that help them survive within their environment. The student is expected to explore, illustrate, and compare life cycles in living organisms such as butterflies, beetles, radishes, or lima beans.

5.10c: The student knows that organisms undergo similar life processes and have structures that help them survive within their environments. The student is expected to describe the differences between complete and incomplete metamorphosis of insects.

Procedures:
This lesson should follow a brief introduction of the butterfly life cycle and is intended to reinforce concepts that have already been introduced.

Before Computer Work Begins

1. If you have not already done so, create either a generic account at Scrapblog for all the students to log into, or make arrangements to create individual accounts for students. (See the *User's Guide to Scrapblog* for more information)
2. Distribute the Student Activity Sheets for students to plan their Scrapblogs. You may want to consider assigning the Student Activity Sheet for homework or completing them in class the day prior to creating the Scrapblog. Allow students plenty of time to complete the activity sheet.
3. Decide whether students will be responsible for obtaining their own images, will use images provided in a shared folder, or will use the ones provided on the CD. If students are using the provided images, upload these files to a shared network location or distribute the files according to your school's procedures.
4. If students are sharing a generic login, then images can also be preloaded into the photo library. This will be especially beneficial for younger students.
5. Decide how the final Scrapblogs will be shared and accessed. Students will provide a link to the online video, or embed the video into another website (like a blog or wiki).
6. Print the necessary sections of the *User's Guide to Scrapblog*.

Computer Activities

1. Remind students of the requirements for this project as stated on the Student Activity Sheet.
    *   Title/Credits Slide
    *   Text to describe each stage of the Butterfly Life Cycle
    *   At least one image representing each stage
2. Guide students in obtaining images either from the ones supplied on the CD (which have been placed in a student-accessible location), from a shared folder or from various image websites (see the introductory section of this book for a list of some sites).
3. Guide students to http://www.scrapblog.com.
4. Have students log on with accounts as determined prior to class.
5. Lead students in beginning a new project, referring to the User's Guide as needed.
6. Demonstrate how to upload the necessary images and use them in the Scrapblog.
7. Demonstrate how to apply text, stickers and other embellishments.
8. Guide students in adding new slides and how to reorder slides as needed.
9. Allow students time to complete the slides according to the sketches on their Student Activity Sheet.
10. Guide students in selecting appropriate music and transitions.
11. Lead students in saving and publishing the Scrapblog, including specific instructions on how to share their projects for assessment purposes.

Name:_____ Date: _____

Butterfly Life Cycle

For this activity, you will create a Scrapblog to illustrate the stages of a butterfly's life. Use photographs and text to explain the process of how a butterfly makes its transformation. Your Scrapblog must include at least one image of each stage of the life cycle, and enough text to explain what happens at each stage. Be sure to include a Title Slide, as well as a citations page to cite the sources of your resources. Use as many slides as you need.

Use this sheet as a guide to help plan for your project. In each box, fill in the appropriate information.

Slide 1: Title

draw a sketch of your slide

Text for slide:

Describe your photograph(s):
1-

2-

Slide 2: Stage 1

draw a sketch of your slide

Text for slide:

Describe your photograph(s):
1-

2-

Slide 3: Stage 2

draw a sketch of your slide

Text for slide:

Describe your photograph(s):
1-

2-

Slide 4: Stage 3

draw a sketch of your slide

Text for slide:

Describe your photograph(s):
1-

2-

Slide 5: Stage 4

draw a sketch of your slide

Text for slide:

Describe your photograph(s):
1-

2-

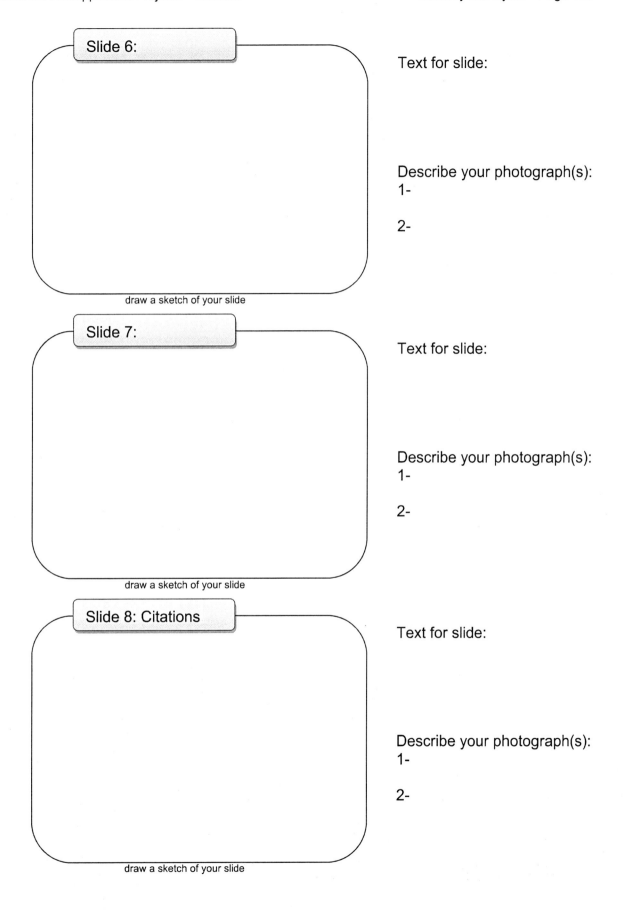

Slide 6:

draw a sketch of your slide

Text for slide:

Describe your photograph(s):
1-

2-

Slide 7:

draw a sketch of your slide

Text for slide:

Describe your photograph(s):
1-

2-

Slide 8: Citations

draw a sketch of your slide

Text for slide:

Describe your photograph(s):
1-

2-

Student Activity
Voki: Dinosaur Mystery

Grade Level: Content Area(s):
Intermediate Science (5-8)

On CD-ROM:
DinosaurSAS.pdf
DinosaurSample.URL (shortcut to completed example – available only online)

Lesson Overview:
Students will use Voki to describe a dinosaur. Students will collect facts about a dinosaur and use the Student Activity Sheet to record these facts. Students will then write scripts to use when recording the voice of their Voki. Finally, students will share their completed Voki with others by embedding it into an available website, or posting the link for others.

Software or Special Materials/Supplies:
Student Activity Sheet
Flash-enabled web browser (Firefox recommended)

Standards:
NSES 5-8 Content Standard C
  • Biological evolution accounts for the diversity of species developed through gradual processes over many generations. Species acquire many of their unique characteristics through biological adaptation, which involves the selection of naturally occurring variations in populations. Biological adaptations include changes in structures, behaviors, or physiology that enhance survival and reproductive success in a particular environment.
  • Extinction of a species occurs when the environment changes and the adaptive characteristics of a species are insufficient to allow its survival. Fossils indicate that many organisms that lived long ago are extinct. Extinction of species is common; most of the species that have lived on the earth no longer exist.

Science TEKS

(Grades 3-5)
9a: The student knows that organisms have characteristics that help them survive and can describe patterns, cycles, systems, and relationships within the environments. The student is expected to observe and describe the physical characteristics of environments and how they support populations and communities within an ecosystem.

10a-b: The student knows that organisms undergo similar life processes and have structures that help them survive within their environments. The student is expected to:
  a. explore how structures and functions of plants and animals allow them to survive in a particular environment.
  b. explore that some characteristics of organisms are inherited such as the number of limbs on an animal or flower color and recognize that some behaviors are learned in response to living in a certain environment such as animals using tools to get food.

7.12a-b: The student knows that living systems at all levels of organization demonstrate the complementary nature of structure and function. The student is expected to:
  a. investigate and explain how internal structures of organisms have adaptations that allow specific functions such as gills in fish, hollow bones in birds, or xylem in plants.
  b. identify the main functions of the systems of the human organism, including the circulatory, respiratory, skeletal, muscular, digestive, excretory, reproductive, integumentary, nervous, and endocrine systems.

Procedures:

This lesson should follow a brief introduction of dinosaur characteristics and is intended to reinforce concepts that have already been introduced.

Before Computer Work Begins

1. Distribute the Student Activity Sheets for students to plan their Voki. You may want to consider assigning the Student Activity Sheet for homework or completing them in class the day prior to creating the Voki. Allow students plenty of time to complete the activity sheet.
2. Determine how the students will create the voice for their Voki. If they will be using microphones, check to make sure they are operational. (see User's Guide as needed)
3. Decide how the final Voki will be shared and accessed. Students will provide a link to the online video, or embed the video into another website (like a blog or wiki).
4. Print the necessary sections of the *User's Guide to Voki*.

Computer Activities

1. Remind students of the requirements for this project as stated on the Student Activity Sheet.
2. Guide students to http://www.voki.com.
3. Lead students in beginning a new project, referring to the User's Guide as needed.
4. Demonstrate how to select a character and to customize the character.
5. Assist students with adding a voice to their character.
6. Allow student to complete their activity, selecting a background and player.
7. Lead students in saving and publishing the Voki, including specific instructions on how to share their projects for assessment purposes.

Name: _____ Date: _____

 # DINOSAUR MYSTERY

Pick a dinosaur to investigate. Find out it's name, what size it was, what it ate, when it lived, where it lived, and some other interesting facts. When you finish, write a script for a mystery Voki. Give at least three facts about your dinosaur without revealing which dinosaur you have. Let others try to decide the identify of your dinosaur!

Use this sheet as a guide to help plan for your project. In each box, fill in the appropriate information. **www.voki.com**

My Dinosaur:

Facts about my dinosaur:

Write your script for the Voki in this box

Student Activity
Animoto Video: Foods from Plant Parts

Grade Level: Content Area(s):
Elementary/Intermediate Science (3-8)

On CD-ROM:
PlantFoodsSAS.pdf
PlantFoodsSample.mp4
Plant Foods Images (folder)
Plant Foods Title Slides (folder)

Lesson Overview:
Students will use Animoto to create a video, using still images and title slides synchronized to a music track to illustrate the foods we eat from various plant parts. Students may either gather images from the Internet or other sources, or may use the ones supplied on the CD (especially if time is limited).
In addition, students will add titles to introduce each plant part. These titles may be added from within Animoto, or may be created using PowerPoint or other similar applications. The music soundtrack may be uploaded by students, or may be chosen from Animoto's music library (recommended). Finally, students will share their completed videos either by downloading the file, embedding the video into an available website, or posting the link for others.

Software or Special Materials/Supplies:
Student Activity Sheet
Animoto Storyboard
Flash-enabled web browser (Firefox recommended)
PowerPoint (optional)
Resources for obtaining images (optional)

Standards:
NSES 5-8 Content Standard C
  • Living systems at all levels of organization demonstrate the complementary nature of structure and function. Important levels of organization for structure and function include cells, organs, tissues, organ systems, whole organisms, and ecosystems.

Science TEKS

3.10a: The student knows that organisms undergo similar life processes and have structures that help them survive within their environments. The student is expected to explore how structures and functions of plants and animals allow them to survive in a particular environment.

7.12c: The student knows that living systems at all levels of organization demonstrate the complementary nature of structure and function. The student is expected to recognize levels of organization in plants and animals, including cells, tissues, organs, organ systems, and organisms.

Procedures:
This lesson should follow a brief introduction of plant parts and is intended for reinforcement.

Before Computer Work Begins

1. If you have not already done so, apply for an educator account at http://www.animoto.com to obtain the registration code for students. This must be done at least a week before the computer activity begins since the application approval process may take several days.
2. To introduce this activity, show the completed Plant Parts Animoto video (PlantFoodsSample.mp4).
3. Distribute the Student Activity Sheet and explain to students that they must give two examples of foods from each of six plant parts in this project.
4. Distribute the blank Animoto Storyboard sheets for students to plan their videos. You may want to consider assigning both the Student Activity Sheet and Animoto Storyboard for homework or completing them in class the day prior to creating the Animoto video.
5. Decide whether students will be responsible for obtaining their own images or will use the ones provided on the CD. If students are using the provided images, upload these files to a shared network location or distribute the files according to standard procedures.
6. Decide whether students will be responsible for creating their own title/description slides or will use the ones provided on the CD. If students are using the provided text slides, upload these files to a shared network location or distribute the files according to standard procedures. Note that the PowerPoint file is included on the CD if you choose to alter the text before saving the slides as .jpg files.
7. Decide how the final Animoto videos will be shared and accessed. Students will either download and turn in the video file, provide a link to the online video, or embed the video into another website (like a blog or wiki).
8. Print the necessary sections of the *User's Guide to Animoto*.

Computer Activities

1. Remind students of the requirements for this project as stated on the Student Activity Sheet.
   - Title & Credits Slides
   - Title slide for each plant part
   - At least two images representing foods from each plant part
2. Guide students in obtaining images, either from the ones supplied on the CD (which have been placed in a student-accessible location) or from various image websites (see the introductory section of this book for a list of some sites).
3. Direct students in creating their title/description slides. Limited title slides can be created within Animoto. However, description slides will need to be created using PowerPoint (or another application). Students may use the provided text slides (.jpg files) or edit the PowerPoint file to create their own.
4. Guide students to http://www.animoto.com.
5. If students have no Animoto accounts, follow the account sign-up procedures outlined in the *User's Guide to Animoto*.
6. Lead students in beginning a new full-length project, referring to the User's Guide as needed.
7. Demonstrate how to upload the necessary images, including any title/description slides (in .jpg format).
8. Allow students time to re-arrange and spotlight images according to their storyboards. If necessary, show students the process of adding title slides from within Animoto.
9. Guide students in selecting appropriate music.
10. Lead students in finalizing the video, including specific instructions on how to share their projects.

Name: _____　　Date: _____

Animoto: Foods from Plant Parts Student Activity Sheet

For this activity, you will create a video using still images and text to illustrate the foods we eat from various parts of the plant (roots, stems, leaves, flowers, seeds, fruits). You must include the following in your Animoto video:

- Title & Credits Slides
- Title slide for each plant part
- At least two images representing foods we eat from each plant part

Use this sheet as a guide to help plan for your project. In each box, draw and label foods that we eat from the corresponding plant parts. Circle any of the foods that <u>you</u> eat.

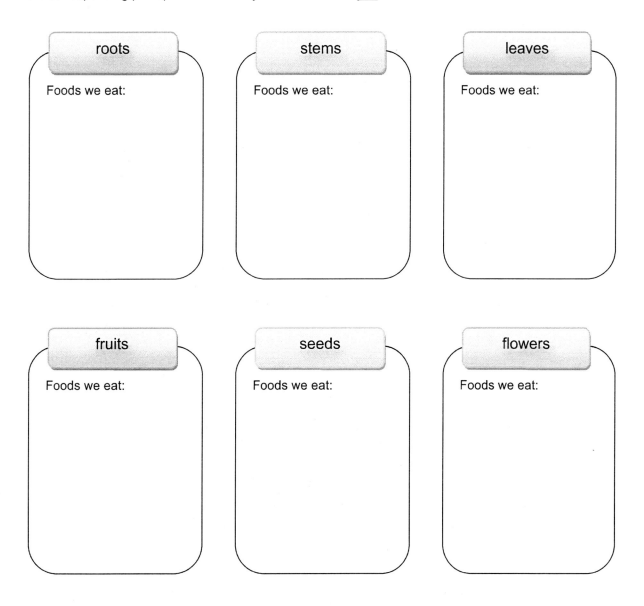

Student Activity
Voki: Photosynthesis

Grade Level: Content Area(s):
Intermediate Science (5-8)

On CD-ROM:
PhotosynthesisSAS.pdf
PhotosynthesisSample.URL (shortcut to completed example – available only online)

Lesson Overview:
Students will use Voki to create a Voki that describes the steps of photosynthesis.
Students will summarize the steps of photosynthesis and use the Student Activity Sheet to record them.
Students will then write scripts to use when recording the voice of their Voki. Finally, students will share their completed Voki with others by embedding it into an available website, or posting the link for others.

Software or Special Materials/Supplies:
Student Activity Sheet
Flash-enabled web browser (Firefox recommended)

Standards:
NSES 5-8 Content Standard C
- For ecosystems, the major source of energy is sunlight. Energy entering ecosystems as sunlight is transferred by producers into chemical energy through photosynthesis. That energy then passes from organism to organism in food webs.

Science TEKS

5.9d: The student knows that there are relationships, systems, and cycles within environments. The student is expected to identify the significance of the carbon dioxide-oxygen cycle to the survival of plants and animals.

7.5a: The student knows that interactions occur between matter and energy. The student is expected to recognize that radiant energy from the Sun is transformed into chemical energy through the process of photosynthesis.

Procedures:
This lesson should follow a brief introduction of photosynthesis and is intended to reinforce concepts that have already been introduced.

Before Computer Work Begins

1. Distribute the Student Activity Sheets for students to plan their Voki. You may want to consider assigning the Student Activity Sheet for homework or completing them in class the day prior to creating the Voki. Allow students plenty of time to complete the activity sheet.
2. Determine how the students will create the voice for their Voki. If they will be using microphones, check to make sure they are operational. (see User's Guide as needed)
3. Decide how the final Voki will be shared and accessed. Students will provide a link to the online video, or embed the video into another website (like a blog or wiki).
4. Print the necessary sections of the *User's Guide to Voki*.

Computer Activities

1. Remind students of the requirements for this project as stated on the Student Activity Sheet.
2. Guide students to http://www.voki.com.
3. Lead students in beginning a new project, referring to the User's Guide as needed.
4. Demonstrate how to select a character and to customize the character.
5. Assist students with adding a voice to their character.
6. Allow student to complete their activity, selecting a background and player.
7. Lead students in saving and publishing the Voki, including specific instructions on how to share their projects for assessment purposes.

Name: _____ Date: _____

Summarize the process of photosynthesis. Create a Voki with those steps. You may need to create more than one to explain all the steps.

Use this sheet as a guide to help plan for your project. In each box, fill in the appropriate information.   **www.voki.com**

Summarize the steps of photosynthesis:

Write your script for the Voki here:

Student Activity
Mixbook: Biomes

Grade Level: Content Area(s):
Elementary/Intermediate Science (3-8)

On CD-ROM:
BiomesSAS.pdf
BiomesSample.URL (shortcut to completed example – available only online)
Biomes Images (folder)

Lesson Overview:
Students will use Mixbook to create an online animated book, using still images, titles, text, and stickers to illustrate and explain characteristics of the terrestrial biomes. Students may either gather images from the Internet or other sources, or may use the ones supplied on the CD (especially if time is limited). Using the storyboard as a guide, students will select appropriate layouts and backgrounds, then enter graphics and text onto the pre-formatted page. Finally, students will share their completed Mixbooks either by embedding the animated book into an available website or by posting the link for others.

Software or Special Materials/Supplies:
Student Activity Sheet
Mixbook Storyboard
Flash-enabled web browser (Firefox recommended)
Resources for obtaining images (optional)

Standards:
NSES 5-8 Content Standard C
- Biological evolution accounts for the diversity of species developed through gradual processes over many generations. Species acquire many of their unique characteristics through biological adaptation, which involves the selection of naturally occurring variations in populations. Biological adaptations include changes in structures, behaviors, or physiology that enhance survival and reproductive success in a particular environment.
- The number of organisms an ecosystem can support depends on the resources available and abiotic factors, such as quantity of light and water, range of temperatures, and soil composition. Given adequate biotic and abiotic resources and no disease or predators, populations (including humans) increase at rapid rates. Lack of resources and other factors, such as predation and climate, limit the growth of populations in specific niches in the ecosystem.

Science TEKS

3.9a: The student knows that organisms have characteristics that help them survive and can describe patterns, cycles, systems, and relationships within the environments. The student is expected to observe and describe the physical characteristics of environments and how they support populations and communities within an ecosystem.

5.9a: The student knows that there are relationships, systems, and cycles within environments The student is expected to observe the way organisms live and survive in their ecosystem by interacting with the living and nonliving elements.

6.12f: The student knows all organisms are classified into Domains and Kingdoms. Organisms within these taxonomic groups share similar characteristics which allow them to interact with the living and nonliving parts of their ecosystem. The student is expected to diagram the levels of organization within an ecosystem, including organism, population, community, and ecosystem.

7.10a: The student knows that there is a relationship between organisms and the environment. The student is expected to observe and describe how different environments, including microhabitats in schoolyards and biomes, support different varieties of organisms.

Procedures:
This lesson should follow a brief introduction of ecology and biomes and is intended for reinforcement.

Before Computer Work Begins

1. To introduce this activity, show the completed sample (BiomesSample.URL on CD).
2. Distribute the Student Activity Sheet and explain to students that they must illustrate and explain the characteristics of the terrestrial biomes in this project. Because different curricula classify these differently, explain to students how many and which ones they must include according to your curriculum.
3. Distribute the blank Mixbook Storyboard sheets for students to plan their books. You may want to consider assigning both the Student Activity Sheet and Mixbook Storyboard for homework or completing them in class the day prior to creating the Mixbook.
4. Decide whether students will be responsible for obtaining their own images or will use the ones provided on the CD. If students are using the provided images, upload these files to a shared network location or distribute the files according to standard procedures.
5. Decide how the final Mixbooks will be shared and accessed. Students will either provide a link to the online book, or embed the book as a widget into another website (like a blog or wiki).
6. Print the necessary sections of the *User's Guide to Mixbook.*

Computer Activities

1. Remind students of the requirements for this project as stated on the Student Activity Sheet.
   - Title & Credits pages
   - 2-page spread for each biome with the following text:
     - Name of biome
     - Description of the climate
     - Examples of plant and animal life
     - Geographic location(s)
   - At least three images representing each biome
2. Guide students in obtaining images, either from the ones supplied on the CD (which have been placed in a student-accessible location) or from various image websites (see the introductory section of this book for a list of some sites).
3. Guide students to http://www.mixbook.com.
4. If students have no Mixbook accounts, follow the account sign-up procedures outlined in the *User's Guide to Mixbook.*
5. Lead students in beginning a new project, referring to the User's Guide as needed.
6. Demonstrate how to upload the necessary images.
7. Walk students through the process of selecting and editing a background.
8. Using the storyboard as a guide, allow students time to add or remove pages as needed. Once the background is selected for either the cover or the first page, it may be best to duplicate that page rather than having to re-create the same background on each page.
9. Guide students in selecting appropriate layouts by practicing with page one.
10. Review, if necessary, how students can add photos or stickers to page one and make needed edits.
11. Demonstrate how to add and edit text elements on page one.
12. Make yourself available as students continue working at their own pace.
13. Lead students in publishing the book, including specific instructions on how to share their projects by linking or embedding.

Name: _____   Date: _____

Mixbook: Biomes

For this activity, you will create a Mixbook animated photo album with images and text to describe the characteristics of each of the biomes. You must include the following in your Mixbook:
- Title & Credits pages
- 2-page spread for each biome with the following text:
  - Name of biome
  - Description of the climate
  - Examples of plant and animal life
  - Geographic location(s)
- At least three images representing each biome

Use this sheet as a guide to help plan for your project. In each box, fill in the appropriate information. Even experts don't necessarily agree on how to classify the various biomes. Your teacher may present more or less biomes than boxes available here.

Biome:

Climate: Plant & Animal Life Examples:

Geographic Location: Image Search Terms:

Biome:

Climate: Plant & Animal Life Examples:

Geographic Location: Image Search Terms:

Biome:

Climate: Plant & Animal Life Examples:

Geographic Location: Image Search Terms:

Biome:

Climate:

Geographic Location:

Plant & Animal Life Examples:

Image Search Terms:

Biome:

Climate:

Geographic Location:

Plant & Animal Life Examples:

Image Search Terms:

Biome:

Climate:

Geographic Location:

Plant & Animal Life Examples:

Image Search Terms:

Biome:

Climate:

Geographic Location:

Plant & Animal Life Examples:

Image Search Terms:

Biome:

Climate:

Geographic Location:

Plant & Animal Life Examples:

Image Search Terms:

Student Activity
Scrapblog: Producers, Consumers & Decomposers

Grade Level: Content Area(s):
Intermediate Science (5-8)

On CD-ROM:
ProducersSAS.pdf
Producer, Consumer & Decomposer Images (folder)
ProducersSample.URL (shortcut to completed example – available only online)

Lesson Overview:
Students will use Scrapblog to create an online scrapbook, using photographs and text synchronized to a music tract to illustrate the role of producers, consumers, and decomposers. Student may either gather images from the Internet or other sources, or may use the ones supplied on the CD (especially if time is limited). Students will use these images and add text to explain what producers, consumers and decomposers do and give some examples. Students will then add other embellishments to their Scrapblog such as stickers, frames, and music from the built-in Scrapblog library. Finally, students will share their completed Scrapblog with others by embedding the video into an available website, or posting the link for others.

Software or Special Materials/Supplies:
Student Activity Sheet
Flash-enabled web browser (Firefox recommended)
Resources for obtaining images (optional)

Standards:
NSES 5-8 Content Standard C
  • Populations of organisms can be categorized by the function they serve in an ecosystem. Plants and some micro-organisms are producers--they make their own food. All animals, including humans, are consumers, which obtain food by eating other organisms. Decomposers, primarily bacteria and fungi, are consumers that use waste materials and dead organisms for food. Food webs identify the relationships among producers, consumers, and decomposers in an ecosystem.

Science TEKS

4.9a: The student knows and understands that living organisms within an ecosystem interact with one another and with their environment. The student is expected to investigate that most producers need sunlight, water, and carbon dioxide to make their own food, while consumers are dependent on other organisms for food.

5.9b: The student knows that there are relationships, systems, and cycles within environments.
The student is expected to describe how the flow of energy derived from the Sun, used by producers to create their own food, is transferred through a food chain and food web to consumers and decomposers.

Procedures:
This lesson should follow a brief introduction of producers, consumers, and decomposers, and is intended to reinforce concepts that have already been introduced.

Before Computer Work Begins

1. If you have not already done so, create either a generic account at Scrapblog for all the students to log into, or make arrangements to create individual accounts for students. (See the *User's Guide to Scrapblog* for more information)
2. Distribute the Student Activity Sheets for students to plan their Scrapblogs. You may want to consider assigning the Student Activity Sheet for homework or completing them in class the day prior to creating the Scrapblog. Allow students plenty of time to complete the activity sheet.
3. Decide whether students will be responsible for obtaining their own images, will use images provided in a shared folder, or will use the ones provided on the CD. If students are using the provided images, upload these files to a shared network location or distribute the files according to your school's procedures.
4. If students are sharing a generic login, then images can also be preloaded into the photo library. This will be especially beneficial for younger students.
5. Decide how the final Scrapblogs will be shared and accessed. Students will provide a link to the online video, or embed the video into another website (like a blog or wiki).
6. Print the necessary sections of the *User's Guide to Scrapblog*.

Computer Activities

1. Remind students of the requirements for this project as stated on the Student Activity Sheet.
   - Title/Credits Slide
   - Text to describe producers, consumers and decomposers
   - At least three images representing three examples of each type (9 total)
2. Guide students in obtaining images, either from the ones supplied on the CD (which have been placed in a student-accessible location), from a shared folder, or from various image websites (see the introductory section of this book for a list of some sites).
3. Guide students to http://www.scrapblog.com.
4. Have students log on with accounts as determined prior to class.
5. Lead students in beginning a new project, referring to the User's Guide as needed.
6. Demonstrate how to upload the necessary images and use them in the Scrapblog.
7. Demonstrate how to apply text, stickers and other embellishments.
8. Guide students in adding new slides and how to reorder slides as needed.
9. Allow students time to complete the slides according to the sketches on their Student Activity Sheet.
10. Guide students in selecting appropriate music and transitions.
11. Lead students in saving and publishing the Scrapblog, including specific instructions on how to share their projects for assessment purposes.

Name: _____   Date: _____

PRODUCERS, CONSUMERS & DECOMPOSERS

For this activity, you will create a Scrapblog to illustrate these three kinds of organisms and how they interact with each other. You will identify the role of each and give at least 3 examples. Each slide will have at least one photograph and some text to explain the role that organism plays. Be sure to include a Title Slide, as well as a citations page to cite the sources of your resources. Use as many slides as you need.

Use this sheet as a guide to help plan for your project. In each box, fill in the appropriate information describing what will be included in the project.

PRODUCERS:

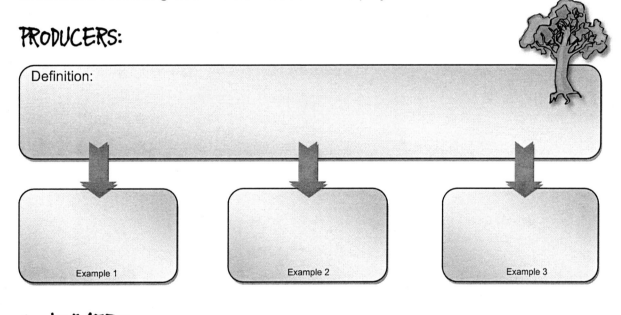

Definition:

Example 1   Example 2   Example 3

CONSUMERS:

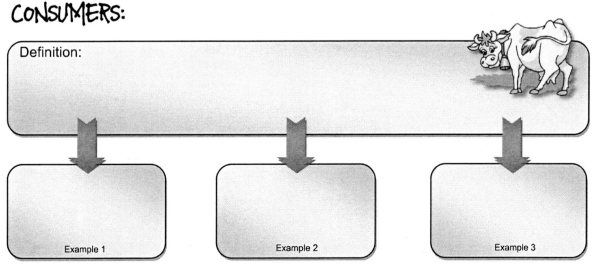

Definition:

Example 1   Example 2   Example 3

DECOMPOSERS:

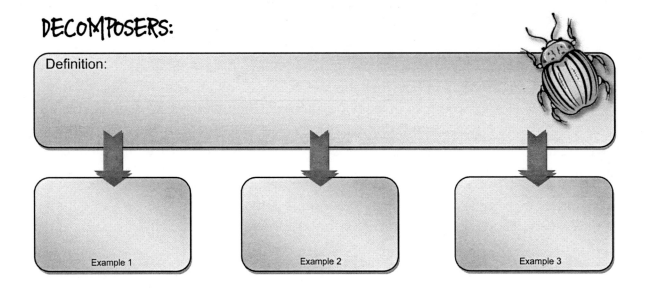

Definition:

Example 1

Example 2

Example 3

Student Activity
TinyPaste: Food Chain

Grade Level: Content Area(s):
Intermediate Science (5-8)

On CD-ROM:
FoodChainSAS1.pdf
FoodChainSAS2.pdf
FoodChainSample.URL (shortcut to completed example – available only online)

Lesson Overview:
Students will use TinyPaste to create a Food Chain of producers and consumers. Students will brainstorm ideas for their food chain and will use a Student Activity Sheet to record these ideas. Students will also find an online image to illustrate each link in the chain, and will use the image and text to create a TinyPaste that includes what eats this link. Students can preview their TinyPaste and make revisions until they are satisfied with the final result. Students then can record the URL of their TinyPaste.

Software or Special Materials/Supplies:
Student Activity Sheet
Flash-enabled web browser (Firefox recommended)

Standards:
NSES 5-8 Content Standard C
- Populations of organisms can be categorized by the function they serve in an ecosystem. Plants and some micro-organisms are producers--they make their own food. All animals, including humans, are consumers, which obtain food by eating other organisms. Decomposers, primarily bacteria and fungi, are consumers that use waste materials and dead organisms for food. Food webs identify the relationships among producers, consumers, and decomposers in an ecosystem.
- For ecosystems, the major source of energy is sunlight. Energy entering ecosystems as sunlight is transferred by producers into chemical energy through photosynthesis. That energy then passes from organism to organism in food webs.
- The number of organisms an ecosystem can support depends on the resources available and abiotic factors, such as quantity of light and water, range of temperatures, and soil composition. Given adequate biotic and abiotic resources and no disease or predators, populations (including humans) increase at rapid rates. Lack of resources and other factors, such as predation and climate, limit the growth of populations in specific niches in the ecosystem.

Science TEKS

(Grades 3-5)
9b: The student knows that there are relationships, systems, and cycles within environments. The student is expected to describe how the flow of energy derived from the Sun, used by producers to create their own food, is transferred through a food chain and food web to consumers and decomposers.

Procedures:
This lesson should follow a brief introduction of food chains and is intended to reinforce concepts that have already been introduced.

Before Computer Work Begins

1. Distribute the Student Activity Sheets for students to plan their TinyPaste. You may want to consider assigning the Student Activity Sheet for homework or completing them in class the day prior to creating the TinyPaste. Allow students plenty of time to complete the activity sheet.
2. Students will need online images to complete this activity. Decide where they will get these images. (See the *User's Guide to TinyPaste*.)
3. Print the necessary sections of the *User's Guide to TinyPaste*.

Computer Activities

1. Remind students of the requirements for this project as stated on the Student Activity Sheet.
2. Guide students to http://www.tinypaste.com.
3. Lead students in beginning a new project, referring to the User's Guide as needed.
4. Demonstrate how to create a TinyPaste including adding an image, increasing text size to make a title, and adding text to describe the insect body part.
5. Lead students in saving and publishing the TinyPaste, including recording the URL.

Name: _____ Date: _____

A food chain explains how food energy is passed between living things. Producers such as plants get their energy from non-living sources, and consumers get their energy from living sources. Complete a food chain that includes at least 5 links in the chain.

Create a TinyPaste for each of the links in your food chain. Each one will contain an image of the animal/plant, facts about that organism, the phrase "is eaten by" and a link to the next link in the chain (except for the last link in the chain).

You will have to start with the last link in the chain so that you'll know the TinyPaste address for the "is eaten by" portion.

http://tinypaste.com

Name of organism	Facts about organism	Is eaten by (tinypaste address)

Food Chain

	Name of Image	Photo credit	URL of image	TinyPaste URL
example	Mist at Beavers Bend	Susan Anderson	http://images2.pics4learning.com/catalog/b/bbrp1.jpg	http://tinypaste.com/76fe3
text	A sudden, quick rainshower in late July cooled the air over 20 degrees in just a few minutes which caused the mist over the river.			
1				
text				
2				
text				
3				
text				
4				
text				
5				
text				

TinyPaste Final URL

Student Activity
BigHugeLabs Trading Cards:
Animal Adaptations

Grade Level: Content Area(s):
Elementary/Intermediate Science (3-8)

On CD-ROM:
AnimalAdaptationsSAS.pdf
AnimalAdaptationsSample.pdf
Animal Adaptations Images (folder)
Animal Adaptations Sample Cards (folder)

Lesson Overview:
Students will use the BigHugeLabs Trading Card generator to create a series of collectible cards, each having an image, title, subtitle, and descriptive text to illustrate and explain how selected animals are adapted to living in their environments. Students may either gather images from the Internet or other sources, or may use the ones supplied on the CD (especially if time is limited). Finally, students will save and share their completed trading cards in print format or by displaying them within a slideshow or document.

Software or Special Materials/Supplies:
Student Activity Sheet
Javascript-enabled web browser (Firefox recommended)
Resources for obtaining images (optional)

Standards:
NSES 5-8 Content Standards A and C
  - Different kinds of questions suggest different kinds of scientific investigations. Some investigations involve observing and describing objects; some involve collecting specimens; some involve seeking more information; some involve discovery of new objects and phenomena.
  - Every organism requires a set of instructions for specifying its traits. Heredity is the passage of these instructions from one generation to another.
  - The characteristics of an organism can be described in terms of a combination of traits. Some traits are inherited and others result from interactions with the environment.
  - All organisms must be able to obtain and use resources, grow, reproduce, and maintain stable internal conditions while living in a constantly changing external environment.
  - An organism's behavior evolves through adaptation to its environment. How a species moves, obtains food, reproduces, and responds to danger are based in the species' evolutionary history.

Science TEKS

(Grades 3-5)
10a: The student knows that organisms undergo similar life processes and have structures that help them survive within their environments. The student is expected to explore how structures and functions of plants and animals allow them to survive in a particular environment.

7.12a: The student knows that living systems at all levels of organization demonstrate the complementary nature of structure and function. The student is expected to investigate and explain how internal structures of organisms have adaptations that allow specific functions such as gills in fish, hollow bones in birds, or xylem in plants.

Procedures:
This lesson should follow a brief introduction of ecology and animal adaptations and is intended for reinforcement.

Before Computer Work Begins

1. To introduce this activity, show the completed sample (AnimalAdaptationsSample.pdf on CD).
2. Distribute the Student Activity Sheet and explain to students that they must create trading cards to describe how five animals are adapted to their environments. You may choose to allow students to choose their own animals, or create a list from which students may choose.
3. Gather a list of resources that students may use to gather information. If you wish to provide a list of animals from which students will choose for this project, it is best to first compile this list of resources, then build the list of animals based on readily available information.
4. You may want to consider assigning the Student Activity Sheet for homework or completing it in class the day prior to creating the trading cards.
5. Decide whether students will be responsible for obtaining their own images or will use the ones provided on the CD. If students are using the provided images, upload these files to a shared network location or distribute the files according to standard procedures.
6. Decide how the final trading cards will be shared and accessed. Students will either print their cards or embed the image files into a slideshow such as PowerPoint or into a word processing document.
7. Print the necessary sections of the *User's Guide to BigHugeLabs Trading Cards*.

Computer Activities

1. Remind students of the requirements for each card in this project as stated on the Student Activity Sheet.
    * Title: Name of the animal
    * Subtitle: The climate or location where the animal is found
    * An image of the animal
    * A description of two of the animal's adaptations
    * Citations for the information and image source
2. Guide students in obtaining images, either from the ones supplied on the CD (which have been placed in a student-accessible location) or from various image websites (see the introductory section of this book for a list of some sites).
3. Guide students to http://bighugelabs.com/deck.php.
4. Lead students in beginning a new project, referring to the User's Guide as needed.
5. Demonstrate how to upload the image.
6. Walk students through the process of selecting cropping options and a background color.
7. Using the Student Activity Sheet as a guide, allow students time to enter the necessary text in the appropriate fields.
8. Guide students in selecting symbols to add to the card (if desired).
9. Demonstrate how to create the card and save or copy it to an appropriate location.
10. Once the collection of cards has been created and saved, give students specific instructions for printing or inserting into a document.

Name: _____   Date: _____

BigHugeLabs Trading Cards: Animal Adaptations

For this activity, you will use the BigHugeLabs Trading Card generator to create **five** cards describing the adaptations of **five** different animals. You must include the following on each card:

- Title: Name of the animal
- Subtitle: The climate or location where the animal is found
- An image of the animal
- A description of two of the animal's adaptations
- Citations for your information and image source

You will save the trading card images so that they can either be printed or embedded into another application such as PowerPoint or Microsoft Word – according to your teacher's directions.

Use this sheet as a guide to help plan for your project. In each box, fill in the appropriate information.

Animal:

Climate or location:

Adaptation #1:

Adaptation #2:

Animal:

Climate or location:

Adaptation #1:

Adaptation #2:

Animal:

Climate or location:

Adaptation #1:

Adaptation #2:

Animal:

Climate or location:

Adaptation #1:

Adaptation #2:

Animal:

Climate or location:

Adaptation #1:

Adaptation #2:

Student Activity
Wordle: Landforms

Grade Level: Content Area(s):
Intermediate Science (5-8)

On CD-ROM:
LandformsSAS.pdf
LandformsSample.jpg

Lesson Overview:
Students will use Wordle to create a word cloud using words and phrases that identify various landforms. Students will brainstorm ideas of types of landforms and will use a Student Activity Sheet to record these ideas. Students will then create their Wordle and will refine the results until they are satisfied with the final result. Students will either print or create a screen capture of the Wordle.

Software or Special Materials/Supplies:
Student Activity Sheet
Flash-enabled web browser (Firefox recommended)

Standards:
NSES 5-8 Content Standard B
  • Landforms are the result of a combination of constructive and destructive forces. Constructive forces include crustal deformation, volcanic eruption, and deposition of sediment, while destructive forces include weathering and erosion.

Science TEKS

3.7c: The student knows that Earth consists of natural resources and its surface is constantly changing. The student is expected to identify and compare different landforms, including mountains, hills, valleys, and plains.

5.7b: The student knows Earth's surface is constantly changing and consists of useful resources. The student is expected to recognize how landforms such as deltas, canyons, and sand dunes are the result of changes to Earth's surface by wind, water, and ice.

Procedures:
This lesson should follow a brief introduction of landforms and is intended to reinforce concepts that have already been introduced.

Before Computer Work Begins

1. Have students use the Landforms Student Activity Sheet to brainstorm words and phrases to describe at least ten types of landforms.
2. Print the necessary sections of the *User's Guide to Wordle*.

Computer Activities

1. Remind students of the requirements for this project as stated on the Student Activity Sheet.
2. Guide students to http://www.wordle.net/create.
3. Lead students in beginning a new project, referring to the User's Guide as needed.
4. Demonstrate how to insert the tilde (~) character between words in a phrase.
5. Demonstrate how to adjust the size of words in the Wordle by increasing the number of times the word is entered into the list.
6. Students will click **Go** to create the Wordle and then will revise the Wordle until a pleasing configuration is found.
7. Students will then print their Wordle, or will use a screen capture to save their Wordle as a .jpg or another format.

Name: _____ Date: _____

Landforms

The earth has a wide variety of features appearing all over the world. List at least ten of the landforms below and then create a Wordle using those landforms. Remember when entering in phrases, they need a tilde (~) between each word to keep them together. For example, **salt marsh** would need to be typed in as **salt~marsh**. Type the title in several times so it is larger than the landforms.

www.wordle.net/create

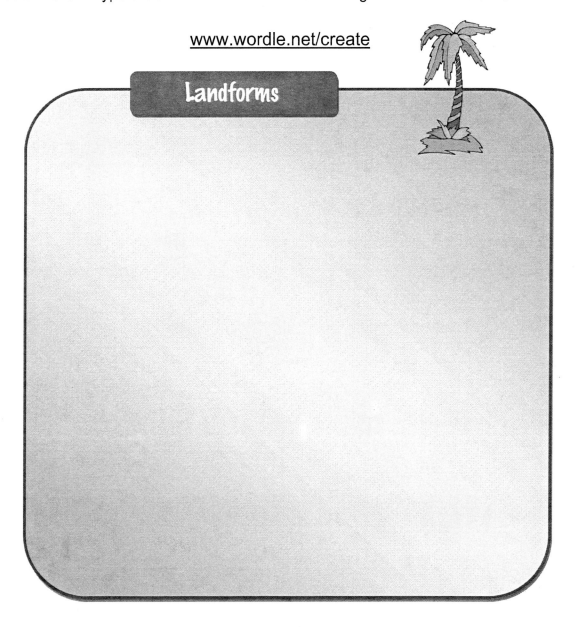

Student Activity
Voki: Forces of Nature

Grade Level: Content Area(s):
Intermediate Science (5-8)

On CD-ROM:
ForcesofNatureSAS.pdf
ForcesofNatureSample.URL (shortcut to completed example –
available only online)

Lesson Overview:
Students will use Voki to create a series of Voki that describe both
constructive and destructive natures. Students will brainstorm constructive and destructive forces and use
the Student Activity Sheet to record them. Students will then write scripts to use when recording the voice
of their Voki. Finally, students will share their completed Voki with others by embedding it into an
available website, or posting the link for others.

Software or Special Materials/Supplies:
Student Activity Sheet
Flash-enabled web browser (Firefox recommended)

Standards:
NSES 5-8 Content Standard D
- Landforms are the result of a combination of constructive and destructive forces.
  Constructive forces include crustal deformation, volcanic eruption, and deposition of
  sediment, while destructive forces include weathering and erosion.
- Lithospheric plates on the scales of continents and oceans constantly move at rates of
  centimeters per year in response to movements in the mantle. Major geological events, such
  as earthquakes, volcanic eruptions, and mountain building, result from these plate motions.

Science TEKS

3.7b: The student knows that Earth consists of natural resources and its surface is constantly changing.
The student is expected to investigate rapid changes in Earth's surface such as volcanic eruptions,
earthquakes, and landslides.

6.10c-d: The student understands the structure of Earth, the rock cycle, and plate tectonics. The student
is expected to:
- c. identify the major tectonic plates, including Eurasian, African, Indo-Australian, Pacific, North
  American, and South American.
- d. describe how plate tectonics causes major geological events such as ocean basins, earthquakes,
  volcanic eruptions, and mountain building.

8.10c: The student knows that climatic interactions exist among Earth, ocean, and weather systems.
The student is expected to identify the role of the oceans in the formation of weather systems such
as hurricanes.

Procedures:
This lesson should follow a brief introduction of constructive and destructive forces and is intended to reinforce concepts that have already been introduced.

Before Computer Work Begins

1. Distribute the Student Activity Sheets for students to plan their Voki. You may want to consider assigning the Student Activity Sheet for homework or completing them in class the day prior to creating the Voki. Allow students plenty of time to complete the activity sheet.
2. Determine how the students will create the voice for their Voki. If they will be using microphones, check to make sure they are operational. (see User's Guide as needed)
3. Decide how the final Voki will be shared and accessed. Students will provide a link to the online video, or embed the video into another website (like a blog or wiki).
4. Print the necessary sections of the *User's Guide to Voki*.

Computer Activities

1. Remind students of the requirements for this project as stated on the Student Activity Sheet.
2. Guide students to http://www.voki.com.
3. Lead students in beginning a new project, referring to the User's Guide as needed.
4. Demonstrate how to select a character and to customize the character.
5. Assist students with adding a voice to their character.
6. Allow student to complete their activity, selecting a background and player.
7. Lead students in saving and publishing the Voki, including specific instructions on how to share their projects for assessment purposes.

Name: _____ Date: _____

FORCES OF NATURE

Nature can be quite forceful in both constructive and destructive ways. List at least 4 examples of each. To create your Voki, select one from each group and create a script that explains how nature is either constructing new environments or destructing existing ones.

Use this sheet as a guide to help plan for your project. In each box, fill in the appropriate information.

www.voki.com

List at least 4 constructive forces:

List at least 4 destructive forces:

Write a script for your Voki describing a constructive force:

Write a script for your Voki describing a destructive force:

Student Activity
Mixbook: Rock Classification & Cycle

Grade Level: Content Area(s):
Elementary/Intermediate Science (3-8)

On CD-ROM:
RockCycleSAS.pdf
RockCycleSample.URL (shortcut to completed example – available only online)
Rock Cycle Images (folder)

Lesson Overview:
Students will use Mixbook to create an online animated book, using still images, titles, text, and stickers to illustrate and describe the rock cycle and how rocks are classified. Students may either gather images from the Internet or other sources, or may use the ones supplied on the CD (especially if time is limited). Using the storyboard as a guide, students will select appropriate layouts and backgrounds, then enter graphics and text onto the pre-formatted page. Finally, students will share their completed Mixbooks either by embedding the animated book into an available website or by posting the link for others.

Software or Special Materials/Supplies:
Student Activity Sheet
Mixbook Storyboard
Flash-enabled web browser (Firefox recommended)
Resources for obtaining images (optional)

Standards:
NSES 5-8 Content Standard D
  • Some changes in the solid earth can be described as the "rock cycle." Old rocks at the earth's surface weather, forming sediments that are buried, then compacted, heated, and often recrystallized into new rock. Eventually, those new rocks may be brought to the surface by the forces that drive plate motions, and the rock cycle continues.

Science TEKS

5.7a: The student knows Earth's surface is constantly changing and consists of useful resources. The student is expected to explore the processes that led to the formation of sedimentary rocks and fossil fuels.

6.10b: The student understands the structure of the Earth, the rock cycle, and plate tectonics. The student is expected to classify rocks as metamorphic, igneous, or sedimentary by the processes of their formation.

Procedures:
This lesson should follow an introduction to rock classification and is intended for reinforcement.

Before Computer Work Begins

1. To introduce this activity, show the completed sample (RockCycleSample.URL on CD).
2. Distribute the Student Activity Sheet and explain to students that they must describe the three types of rock classifications and how they can be transformed into other types through the rock cycle.
3. Distribute the blank Mixbook Storyboard sheets for students to plan their books. You may want to consider assigning both the Student Activity Sheet and Mixbook Storyboard for homework or completing them in class the day prior to creating the Mixbook.
4. Decide whether students will be responsible for obtaining their own images or will use the ones provided on the CD. If students are using the provided images, upload these files to a shared network location or distribute the files according to standard procedures.
5. Decide how the final Mixbooks will be shared and accessed. Students will either provide a link to the online book, or embed the book as a widget into another website (like a blog or wiki).
6. Print the necessary sections of the *User's Guide to Mixbook*.

Computer Activities

1. Remind students of the requirements for this project as stated on the Student Activity Sheet.
   - Title & Credits pages
   - 2-page spread for each rock type with the following text:
     - Name of rock type
     - How this type of rock forms
     - How this type of rock can be transformed into the other types
     - At least three common examples
   - At least three images representing each rock type along with captions
2. Guide students in obtaining images, either from the ones supplied on the CD (which have been placed in a student-accessible location) or from various image websites (see the introductory section of this book for a list of some sites).
3. Guide students to http://www.mixbook.com.
4. If students have no Mixbook accounts, follow the account sign-up procedures outlined in the *User's Guide to Mixbook*.
5. Lead students in beginning a new project, referring to the User's Guide as needed.
6. Demonstrate how to upload the necessary images.
7. Walk students through the process of selecting and editing a background.
8. Using the storyboard as a guide, allow students time to add or remove pages as needed. Once the background is selected for either the cover or the first page, it may be best to duplicate that page rather than having to re-create the same background on each page.
9. Guide students in selecting appropriate layouts by practicing with page one.
10. Review, if necessary, how students can add photos or stickers to page one and make needed edits.
11. Demonstrate how to add and edit text elements on page one.
12. Make yourself available as students continue working at their own pace.
13. Lead students in publishing the book, including specific instructions on how to share their projects by linking or embedding.

Name: _____   Date: _____

Mixbook: Rock Classification & Cycle

For this activity, you will create a Mixbook animated photo album with images and text to describe the three types of rock classifications and how they can be transformed into other types through the rock cycle. You must include the following in your Mixbook:
- Title & Credits pages
- 2-page spread for each rock type with the following text:
  - Name of rock type
  - How this type of rock forms
  - How this type of rock can be transformed into the other types
  - At least three common examples
- At least three images representing each rock type along with captions

Use this sheet as a guide to help plan for your project. In each box, fill in the appropriate information.

Rock Type:

How it's formed: How it can be transformed:

Examples: Image Search Terms:

Rock Type:

How it's formed: How it can be transformed:

Examples: Image Search Terms:

Rock Type:

How it's formed: How it can be transformed:

Examples: Image Search Terms:

Student Activity
Voki: Characteristics of the Moon

Grade Level: Content Area(s):
Intermediate Science (5-8)

On CD-ROM:
MoonSAS.pdf
MoonSample.URL (shortcut to completed example – available only online)

Lesson Overview:
Students will use Voki to create a series of Voki that describe the characteristics
of the Moon. Students will collect facts about the moon and use the Student
Activity Sheet to record these facts. Students will then write scripts to use when
recording the voice of their Voki. Finally, students will share their completed Voki with others by
embedding it into an available website, or posting the link for others.

Software or Special Materials/Supplies:
Student Activity Sheet
Flash-enabled web browser (Firefox recommended)

Standards:
NSES 5-8 Content Standard D
- Most objects in the solar system are in regular and predictable motion. Those motions explain
  such phenomena as the day, the year, phases of the moon, and eclipses.

Science TEKS

3.3c: The student knows that information, critical thinking, scientific problem solving, and the contributions
of scientists are used in making decisions. The student is expected to represent the natural world using
models such as volcanoes or Sun, Earth, and Moon system and identify their limitations, including size,
properties, and materials.

(Grades 3-4)
8c: The student knows that there are recognizable patterns in the natural world and among the Sun,
Earth, and Moon system. The student is expected to collect and analyze data to identify sequences and
predict patterns of change in shadows, tides, seasons, and the observable appearance of the Moon over
time.

5.8d: The student knows that there are recognizable patterns in the natural world and among the Sun,
Earth, and Moon system. The student is expected to identify and compare the physical characteristics of
the Sun, Earth, and Moon.

Procedures:
This lesson should follow a brief introduction of moon characteristics and is intended to reinforce concepts that have already been introduced.

Before Computer Work Begins

1. Distribute the Student Activity Sheets for students to plan their Voki. You may want to consider assigning the Student Activity Sheet for homework or completing them in class the day prior to creating the Voki. Allow students plenty of time to complete the activity sheet.
2. Determine how the students will create the voice for their Voki. If they will be using microphones, check to make sure they are operational. (see User's Guide as needed)
3. Decide how the final Voki will be shared and accessed. Students will provide a link to the online video, or embed the video into another website (like a blog or wiki).
4. Print the necessary sections of the *User's Guide to Voki*.

Computer Activities

1. Remind students of the requirements for this project as stated on the Student Activity Sheet.
2. Guide students to http://www.voki.com.
3. Lead students in beginning a new project, referring to the User's Guide as needed.
4. Demonstrate how to select a character and to customize the character.
5. Assist students with adding a voice to their character.
6. Allow student to complete their activity, selecting a background and player.
7. Lead students in saving and publishing the Voki, including specific instructions on how to share their projects for assessment purposes.

Name: _____ Date: _____

CHARACTERISTICS OF THE MOON

Find out about these characteristics of the moon and use them to make a series of Voki. Choose a character that can tell others about the moon, and give it a voice – either your own, or one built into Voki. Use this sheet as a guide to help plan for your project.
In each box, fill in the appropriate information.

www.voki.com

Facts about the Moon	Write your script for the Voki in this box
Distance from the earth:	
Mass & Density:	
Temperature:	

Gravity on the moon:

_____
_____
_____
_____
_____

Moon Phases:

_____
_____
_____
_____
_____

How the moon affects the tides:

_____
_____
_____
_____
_____

Craters:

_____
_____
_____
_____
_____

A fun fact you learned about the moon:

_____
_____
_____
_____
_____

Student Activity
Voki: Ocean Tides

Grade Level: Content Area(s):
Intermediate Science (5-8)

On CD-ROM:
TidesSAS.pdf
TidesSample.URL (shortcut to completed example – available only online)

Lesson Overview:
Students will use Voki to create a series of Voki that describe the characteristics of the ocean tides. Students will collect facts about the tides and use the Student Activity Sheet to create the scripts to record the voice of their Voki. Finally, students will share their completed Voki with others by embedding it into an available website, or posting the link for others.

Software or Special Materials/Supplies:
Student Activity Sheet
Flash-enabled web browser (Firefox recommended)

Standards:
NSES 5-8 Content Standard D
- Gravity is the force that keeps planets in orbit around the sun and governs the rest of the motion in the solar system. Gravity alone holds us to the earth's surface and explains the phenomena of the tides.
- The sun is the major source of energy for phenomena on the earth's surface, such as growth of plants, winds, ocean currents, and the water cycle. Seasons result from variations in the amount of the sun's energy hitting the surface, due to the tilt of the earth's rotation on its axis and the length of the day.

Science TEKS

4.8c: The student knows that there are recognizable patterns in the natural world and among the Sun, Earth, and Moon system. The student is expected to collect and analyze data to identify sequences and predict patterns of change in shadows, tides, seasons, and the observable appearance of the Moon over time.

8.7c: The student knows the effects resulting from cyclical movements of the Sun, Earth, and Moon. The student is expected to relate the position of the Moon and Sun to their effect on ocean tides.

Procedures:
This lesson should follow a brief introduction of ocean tides and is intended to reinforce concepts that have already been introduced.

Before Computer Work Begins

1. Distribute the Student Activity Sheets for students to plan their Voki. You may want to consider assigning the Student Activity Sheet for homework or completing them in class the day prior to creating the Voki. Allow students plenty of time to complete the activity sheet.
2. Determine how the students will create the voice for their Voki. If they will be using microphones, check to make sure they are operational. (See the User's Guide as needed.)
3. Decide how the final Voki will be shared and accessed. Students will provide a link to the online video, or embed the video into another website (like a blog or wiki).
4. Print the necessary sections of the *User's Guide to Voki.*

Computer Activities

1. Remind students of the requirements for this project as stated on the Student Activity Sheet.
2. Guide students to http://www.voki.com.
3. Lead students in beginning a new project, referring to the User's Guide as needed.
4. Demonstrate how to select a character and to customize the character.
5. Assist students with adding a voice to their character.
6. Allow student to complete their activity, selecting a background and player.
7. Lead students in saving and publishing the Voki, including specific instructions on how to share their projects for assessment purposes.

Name: _____ Date: _____

Ocean Tides

The level of the ocean on earth is affected by several factors. Create a script to record a series of Voki that discuss the factors that contribute to the ocean's tides.

Be sure to include:

- What are tides and how do they work?
- Are tides in all parts of the world the same?
- What's the difference between spring tides and neap tides?

www.voki.com

Create the scripts for your Voki here:

Student Activity
BigHugeLabs Trading Cards: The Eight Planets

Grade Level: Content Area(s):
Elementary/Intermediate Science (3-8)

On CD-ROM:
PlanetsSAS.pdf
PlanetsSample.pdf
Planets Images (folder)
Planets Sample Cards (folder)

Lesson Overview:
Students will use the BigHugeLabs Trading Card generator to create a series of collectible cards, each having an image, title, subtitle, and descriptive text to describe each of the eight planets. Students may either gather images from the Internet or other sources, or may use the ones supplied on the CD (especially if time is limited). Finally, students will save and share their completed trading cards in print format or by displaying them within a slideshow or document.

Software or Special Materials/Supplies:
Student Activity Sheet
Javascript-enabled web browser (Firefox recommended)
Resources for obtaining images (optional)

Standards:
NSES 5-8 Content Standard D
- The earth is the third planet from the sun in a system that includes the moon, the sun, eight other planets and their moons, and smaller objects, such as asteroids and comets. The sun, an average star, is the central and largest body in the solar system.
- Most objects in the solar system are in regular and predictable motion. Those motions explain such phenomena as the day, the year, phases of the moon, and eclipses.

Science TEKS

3.8d: The student knows there are recognizable patterns in the natural world and among objects in the sky. The student is expected to identify the planets in Earth's solar system and their position in relation to the Sun.

6.11a: The student understands the organization of our solar system and the relationships among the various bodies that comprise it. The student is expected to describe the physical properties, locations, and movements of the Sun, planets, Galilean moons, meteors, asteroids, and comets.

8.8b: The student knows characteristics of the universe. The student is expected to recognize that the Sun is a medium-sized star near the edge of a disc-shaped galaxy of stars and that the Sun is many thousands of times closer to Earth than any other star.

Procedures:
This lesson should follow an introduction to the eight planets and is intended for reinforcement and practice.

Before Computer Work Begins

1. To introduce this activity, show the completed sample (PlanetsSample.pdf on CD).
2. Distribute the Student Activity Sheet and explain to students that they must create trading cards to describe each of the eight planets.
3. Gather a list of resources that students may use to obtain information.
4. You may want to consider assigning the Student Activity Sheet for homework or completing it in class the day prior to creating the trading cards.
5. Decide whether students will be responsible for obtaining their own images or will use the ones provided on the CD. Planet images are readily available (and usually fall under Fair Use Guidelines) at government-funded sites such as NASA.
6. Decide how the final trading cards will be shared and accessed. Students will either print their cards or embed the image files into a slideshow such as PowerPoint or into a word processing document.
7. Print the necessary sections of the *User's Guide to BigHugeLabs Trading Cards*.

Computer Activities

1. Remind students of the requirements for each card in this project as stated on the Student Activity Sheet.
   - Title: Name of the planet
   - Subtitle: Ranking order in terms of distance from the sun (ex: "4th planet from the sun")
   - An image of the planet
   - The length of the year of the planet (in Earth days)
   - Three facts about the planet
   - Citations for the information and image source
2. Guide students in obtaining images, either from the ones supplied on the CD (which have been placed in a student-accessible location) or from various image websites (see the introductory section of this book for a list of some sites).
3. Guide students to http://bighugelabs.com/deck.php.
4. Lead students in beginning a new project, referring to the User's Guide as needed.
5. Demonstrate how to upload the image.
6. Walk students through the process of selecting cropping options and a background color.
7. Using the Student Activity Sheet as a guide, allow students time to enter the necessary text in the appropriate fields.
8. Guide students in selecting symbols to add to the card (if desired).
9. Demonstrate how to create the card and save or copy it to an appropriate location.
10. Once the collection of cards has been created and saved, give students specific instructions for printing or inserting into a document.

Name: _____   Date: _____

BigHugeLabs Trading Cards: The 8 Planets

For this activity, you will use the BigHugeLabs Trading Card generator to create **eight** cards describing the eight planets in our solar system. You must include the following on each card:

- Title: Name of the planet
- Subtitle: Ranking order in terms of distance from the sun (ex: "4th planet from the sun")
- An image of the planet
- The length of the year of the planet (in Earth days)
- Three facts about the planet
- Citations for your information and image source

You will save the trading card images so that they can either be printed or embedded into another application such as PowerPoint or Microsoft Word – according to your teacher's directions.

Use this sheet as a guide to help plan for your project. In each box, fill in the appropriate information.

Ranking order:

Fact #1:

Fact #2:

Fact #3:

Length of year:

Planet:

Ranking order:

Fact #1:

Fact #2:

Fact #3:

Length of year:

Planet:

Ranking order:

Fact #1:

Fact #2:

Fact #3:

Length of year:

Planet:

Ranking order:

Fact #1:

Fact #2:

Fact #3:

Length of year:

Planet:

Ranking order:

Fact #1:

Fact #2:

Fact #3:

Length of year:

Planet:

Ranking order:

Fact #1:

Fact #2:

Fact #3:

Length of year:

Planet:

Ranking order:

Fact #1:

Fact #2:

Fact #3:

Length of year:

Planet:

Ranking order:

Fact #1:

Fact #2:

Fact #3:

Length of year:

Planet:

Student Activity
Scrapblog: States of Matter

Grade Level: Content Area(s):
Intermediate Science (5-8)

On CD-ROM:
MatterStatesSAS.pdf
States of Matter Images (folder)
MatterStatesSample.URL (shortcut to completed example – available only online)

Lesson Overview:
Students will use Scrapblog to create an online scrapbook, using photographs and text synchronized to a music track to illustrate the different states of matter. Student may either gather images from the Internet or other sources, or may use the ones supplied on the CD (especially if time is limited). Students will use these images and add text to explain the processes of transformation between the states. Students will then add other embellishments to their Scrapblog such as stickers, frames, and music from the built-in Scrapblog library. Finally, students will share their completed Scrapblog with others by embedding the video into an available website, or posting the link for others.

Software or Special Materials/Supplies:
Student Activity Sheet
Flash-enabled web browser (Firefox recommended)
Resources for obtaining images (optional)

Standards:
NSES 5-8 Content Standard B
- A substance has characteristic properties, such as density, a boiling point, and solubility, all of which are independent of the amount of the sample.
- Energy is a property of many substances and is associated with heat, light, electricity, mechanical motion, sound, nuclei, and the nature of a chemical. Energy is transferred in many ways.

Science TEKS

(Grades 3-5)
5a-b: The student knows that matter has measurable physical properties and those properties determine how matter is classified, changed, and used. The student is expected to:
  a. measure, compare, and contrast physical properties of matter, including size, mass, volume, states (solid, liquid, gas), temperature, magnetism, and the ability to sink or float.
  b. predict the changes caused by heating and cooling such as ice becoming liquid water and condensation forming on the outside of a glass of ice water.

Procedures:
This lesson should follow a brief introduction of the states of matter and is intended to reinforce concepts that have already been introduced.

Before Computer Work Begins

1. If you have not already done so, create either a generic account at Scrapblog for all the students to log into, or make arrangements to create individual accounts for students. (See the *User's Guide to Scrapblog* for more information.)
2. Distribute the Student Activity Sheets for students to plan their Scrapblogs. You may want to consider assigning the Student Activity Sheet for homework or completing them in class the day prior to creating the Scrapblog. Allow students plenty of time to complete the activity sheet.
3. Decide whether students will be responsible for obtaining their own images, will use images provided in a shared folder, or will use the ones provided on the CD. If students are using the provided images, upload these files to a shared network location or distribute the files according to your school's procedures.
4. If students are sharing a generic login, then images can be preloaded into the photo library. This will be especially beneficial for younger students.
5. Decide how the final Scrapblogs will be shared and accessed. Students will provide a link to the online video, or embed the video into another website (like a blog or wiki).
6. Print the necessary sections of the *User's Guide to Scrapblog*.

Computer Activities

1. Remind students of the requirements for this project as stated on the Student Activity Sheet.
   - Title/Credits Slide
   - Text to describe each stage of the states of matter
   - At least one image representing each stage
2. Guide students in obtaining images, either from the ones supplied on the CD (which have been placed in a student-accessible location), from a shared folder, or from various image websites (see the introductory section of this book for a list of some sites).
3. Guide students to http://www.scrapblog.com.
4. Have students log on with accounts as determined prior to class.
5. Lead students in beginning a new project, referring to the User's Guide as needed.
6. Demonstrate how to upload the necessary images and use them in the Scrapblog.
7. Demonstrate how to apply text, stickers and other embellishments.
8. Guide students in adding new slides, and how to reorder slides as needed.
9. Allow students time to complete the slides according to the sketches on their Student Activity Sheet.
10. Guide students in selecting appropriate music and transitions.
11. Lead students in saving and publishing the Scrapblog, including specific instructions on how to share their projects for assessment purposes.

Name: _____ Date: _____

States of Matter

Matter changes states when special forces such as temperature are added. For this activity, you will create a Scrapblog to show the changes that occur with a change of temperature. Your Scrapblog must include at least one image of each state of matter, and enough text to explain what happens at each stage. Be sure to include a Title Slide, as well as a citations page to cite the sources of your resources. Use as many slides as you need.

Use this sheet as a guide to help plan for your project. In each box, fill in the appropriate information.

Slide 1: Title

draw a sketch of your slide

Text for slide:

Describe your photograph(s):
1-

2-

Slide 2:

draw a sketch of your slide

Text for slide:

Describe your photograph(s):
1-

2-

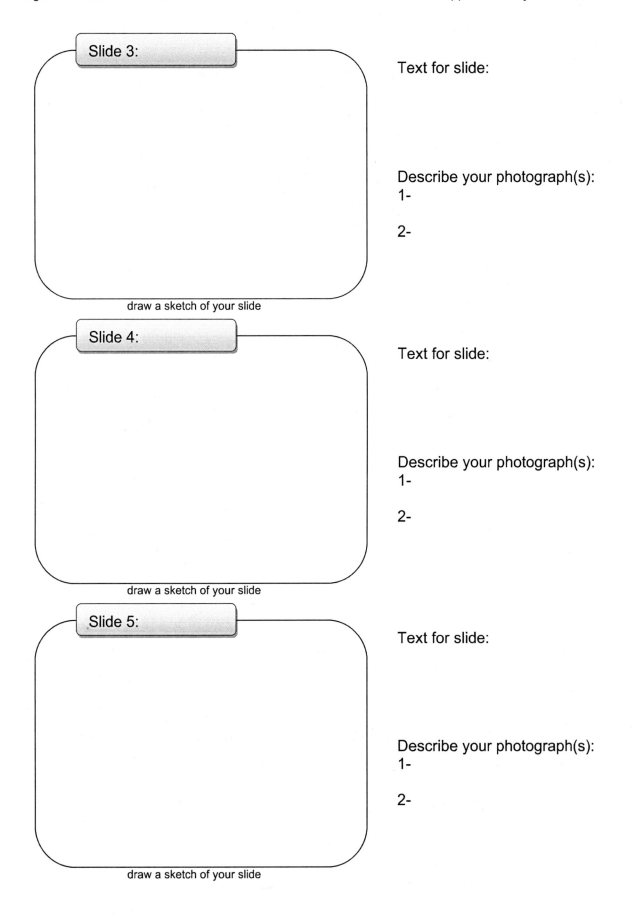

Slide 3:

draw a sketch of your slide

Text for slide:

Describe your photograph(s):
1-

2-

Slide 4:

draw a sketch of your slide

Text for slide:

Describe your photograph(s):
1-

2-

Slide 5:

draw a sketch of your slide

Text for slide:

Describe your photograph(s):
1-

2-

Slide 6:

draw a sketch of your slide

Text for slide:

Describe your photograph(s):
1-

2-

Slide 7:

draw a sketch of your slide

Text for slide:

Describe your photograph(s):
1-

2-

Slide 8: Citations

draw a sketch of your slide

Text for slide:

Describe your photograph(s):
1-

2-

Student Activity
Animoto Video: Energy Forms

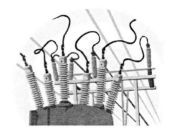

Grade Level: Content Area(s):
Intermediate Science (5-8)

On CD-ROM:
EnergyFormsSAS.pdf
EnergyFormsSample.mp4
Energy Forms Images (folder)
Energy Forms Title Slides (folder)

Lesson Overview:
Students will use Animoto to create a video using still images and title slides synchronized to a music track to illustrate and explain four of the various forms of energy. Students may either gather images from the Internet or other sources, or may use the ones supplied on the CD (especially if time is limited). In addition, students will add titles to introduce and explain each of the chosen energy forms. These titles may be added from within Animoto or may be created using PowerPoint or other similar applications. The music soundtrack may be uploaded by students or may be chosen from Animoto's music library (recommended). Finally, students will share their completed videos either by downloading the file, embedding the video into an available website, or posting the link for others.

Software or Special Materials/Supplies:
Student Activity Sheet
Animoto Storyboard
Flash-enabled web browser (Firefox recommended)
PowerPoint (optional)
Resources for obtaining images (optional)

Standards:
NSES 5-8 Content Standard B
  • Energy is transferred in many ways.
  • Heat moves in predictable ways, flowing from warmer objects to cooler ones, until both reach the same temperature.
  • In most chemical and nuclear reactions, energy is transferred into or out of a system.

Science TEKS

(Grades 3-5)
6a: The student knows that energy occurs in many forms and can be observed in cycles, patterns, and systems. The student is expected to explore the uses of energy, including mechanical, light, thermal, electrical, and sound energy.

Procedures:
This lesson should follow a brief introduction of the various forms of energy and is intended to reinforce concepts that have already been introduced.

Before Computer Work Begins

1. If you have not already done so, apply for an educator account at http://www.animoto.com to obtain the registration code for students. This must be done at least a week before the computer activity begins since the application approval process may take several days.
2. To introduce this activity, show the completed Energy Forms Animoto video. (EnergyFormsSample.mp4)
3. Distribute the Student Activity Sheet and explain to students that they must choose four energy forms to include in this project. Allow students plenty of time to complete the activity sheet.
4. Distribute the blank Animoto Storyboard sheets for students to plan their videos. You may want to consider assigning both the Student Activity Sheet and Animoto Storyboard for homework or completing them in class the day prior to creating the Animoto video.
5. Decide whether students will be responsible for obtaining their own images or will use the ones provided on the CD. If students are using the provided images, upload these files to a shared network location or distribute the files according to standard procedures.
6. Decide whether students will be responsible for creating their own title/description slides or will use the ones provided on the CD. If students are using the provided text slides, upload these files to a shared network location or distribute the files according to standard procedures. Note that the PowerPoint file is included on the CD if you choose to alter the text before saving the slides as .jpg files.
7. Decide how the final Animoto videos will be shared and accessed. Students will either download and turn in the video file, provide a link to the online video, or embed the video into another website (like a blog or wiki).
8. Print the necessary sections of the *User's Guide to Animoto*.

Computer Activities

1. Remind students of the requirements for this project as stated on the Student Activity Sheet.
   - Title/Credits Slide
   - Title slide for each form of energy
   - Definition or properties slide for each form of energy
   - At least two images representing each form of energy
2. Guide students in obtaining images, either from the ones supplied on the CD (which have been placed in a student-accessible location) or from various image websites (see the introductory section of this book for a list of some sites).
3. Direct students in creating their title/description slides. Limited title slides can be created within Animoto. However, description slides will need to be created using PowerPoint (or another application). Students may use the provided text slides (.jpg files) or edit the PowerPoint file to create their own.
4. Guide students to http://www.animoto.com.
5. If students have no Animoto accounts, follow the account sign-up procedures outlined in the *User's Guide to Animoto*.
6. Lead students in beginning a new full-length project, referring to the User's Guide as needed.
7. Demonstrate how to upload the necessary images, including any title/description slides (in .jpg format).
8. Allow students time to re-arrange and spotlight images according to their storyboards. If necessary, show students the process of adding title slides from within Animoto.
9. Guide students in selecting appropriate music.
10. Lead students in finalizing the video, including specific instructions on how to share their projects.

Name: _____   Date: _____

Animoto: Energy Forms Student Activity Sheet

For this activity, you will create a video using still images and text to show your understanding of the different forms of energy. You will choose at least four energy forms to include in the video. You must include the following in your Animoto video:

- Title/Credits Slide
- Title slide for each form of energy
- Definition or properties slide for each form of energy
- At least two images representing each form of energy

Use this sheet as a guide to help plan for your project. In each box, fill in the appropriate information.

Energy Form:	Definition or Properties:	Image Search Terms:

Energy Form:	Definition or Properties:	Image Search Terms:

Energy Form:	Definition or Properties:	Image Search Terms:

Energy Form:	Definition or Properties:	Image Search Terms:

Student Activity
Scrapblog: Electromagnetic Spectrum

Grade Level: Content Area(s):
Intermediate Science (5-8)

On CD-ROM:
ElectromagneticSAS.pdf
Electromagnetic Spectrum Images (folder)
ElectromagneticSample.URL (shortcut to completed example – available only online)

Lesson Overview:
Students will use Scrapblog to create an online scrapbook, using photographs and text synchronized to a music track to illustrate the electromagnetic spectrum. Student may either gather images from the Internet or other sources, or may use the ones supplied on the CD (especially if time is limited). Students will use these images and add text to explain the regions of the spectrum. Students will then add other embellishments to their Scrapblog such as stickers, frames, and music from the built-in Scrapblog library. Finally, students will share their completed Scrapblog with others by embedding the video into an available website, or posting the link for others.

Software or Special Materials/Supplies:
Student Activity Sheet
Flash-enabled web browser (Firefox recommended)
Resources for obtaining images (optional)

Standards:
NSES 5-8 Content Standard B
- The sun is a major source of energy for changes on the earth's surface. The sun loses energy by emitting light. A tiny fraction of that light reaches the earth, transferring energy from the sun to the earth. The sun's energy arrives as light with a range of wavelengths, consisting of visible light, infrared, and ultraviolet radiation.

Science TEKS

8.8c: The student knows characteristics of the universe. The student is expected to explore how different wavelengths of the electromagnetic spectrum such as light and radio waves are used to gain information about distances and properties of components in the universe.

Procedures:
This lesson should follow a brief introduction of the electromagnetic spectrum and is intended to reinforce concepts that have already been introduced.

Before Computer Work Begins

1. If you have not already done so, create either a generic account at Scrapblog for all the students to log into, or make arrangements to create individual accounts for students. (See the *User's Guide to Scrapblog* for more information.)
2. Distribute the Student Activity Sheets for students to plan their Scrapblogs. You may want to consider assigning the Student Activity Sheet for homework or completing them in class the day prior to creating the Scrapblog. Allow students plenty of time to complete the activity sheet.
3. Decide whether students will be responsible for obtaining their own images, will use images provided in a shared folder, or will use the ones provided on the CD. If students are using the provided images, upload these files to a shared network location or distribute the files according to your school's procedures.
4. If students are sharing a generic login, then images can also be preloaded into the photo library. This will be especially beneficial for younger students.
5. Decide how the final Scrapblogs will be shared and accessed. Students will provide a link to the online video, or embed the video into another website (like a blog or wiki).
6. Print the necessary sections of the *User's Guide to Scrapblog*.

Computer Activities

1. Remind students of the requirements for this project as stated on the Student Activity Sheet.
    *   Title/Credits Slide
    *   Text to describe each region of the electromagnetic spectrum
    *   At least one image representing each region
2. Guide students in obtaining images, either from the ones supplied on the CD (which have been placed in a student-accessible location), from a shared folder, or from various image websites (see the introductory section of this book for a list of some sites).
3. Guide students to http://www.scrapblog.com.
4. Have students log on with accounts as determined prior to class.
5. Lead students in beginning a new project, referring to the User's Guide as needed.
6. Demonstrate how to upload the necessary images and use them in the Scrapblog.
7. Demonstrate how to apply text, stickers and other embellishments.
8. Guide students in adding new slides and how to reorder slides as needed.
9. Allow students time to complete the slides according to the sketches on their Student Activity Sheet.
10. Guide students in selecting appropriate music and transitions.
11. Lead students in saving and publishing the Scrapblog, including specific instructions on how to share their projects for assessment purposes.

Name: _____ Date: _____

Electromagnetic Spectrum

For this activity, you will create a Scrapblog to illustrate the different regions of the spectrum. Make one slide for each region, which will include information about the different types and will have at least one photograph as an example. Be sure to include a Title Slide, as well as a citations page to cite the sources of your resources. Use as many slides as you need.

Use this sheet as a guide to help plan for your project. In each box, fill in the appropriate information.

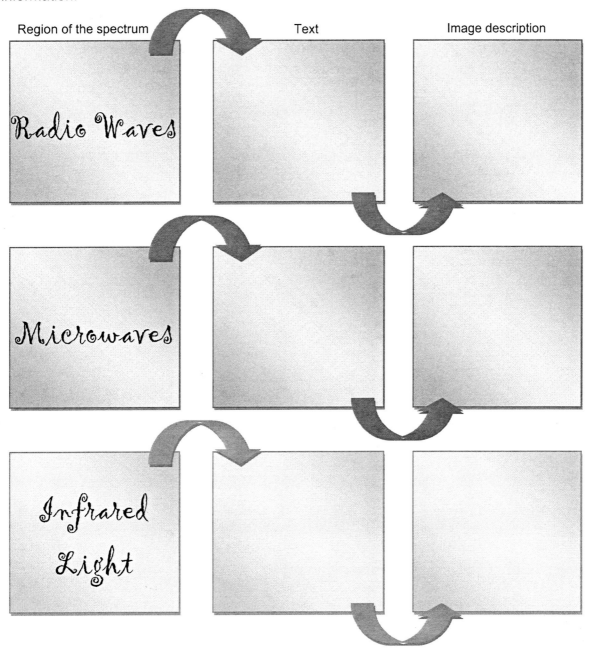

Region of the spectrum	Text	Image description
Radio Waves		
Microwaves		
Infrared Light		

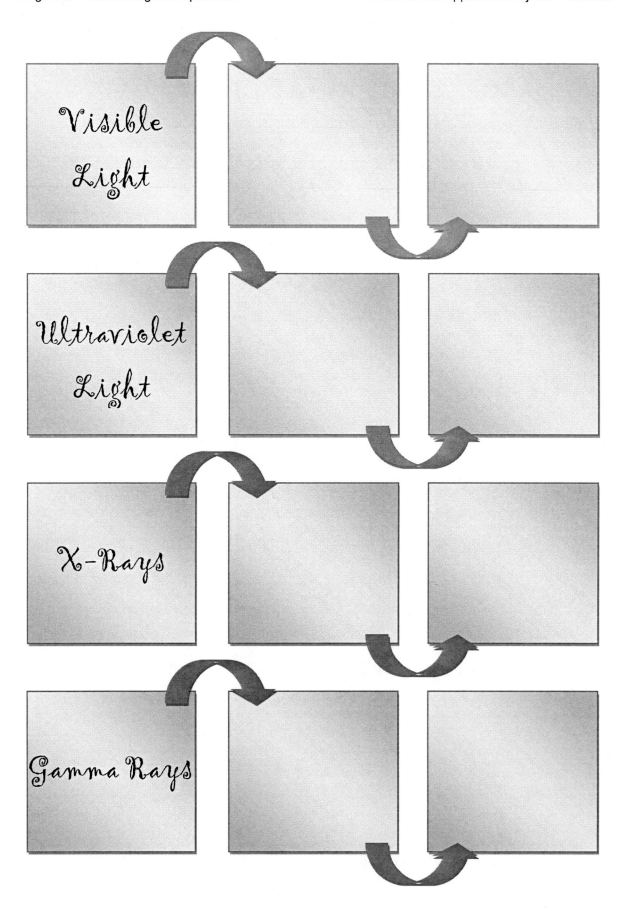

Visible Light

Ultraviolet Light

X-Rays

Gamma Rays

Student Activity
Mixbook: Simple Machines

Grade Level: Content Area(s):
Elementary/Intermediate Science (3-8)

On CD-ROM:
SimpleMachinesSAS.pdf
SimpleMachinesSample.URL (shortcut to completed example – available only online)
Simple Machines Images (folder)

Lesson Overview:
Students will use Mixbook to create an online animated book, using still images, titles, text, and stickers to illustrate, explain, and give common examples of each type of the simple machines. Students may either gather images from the Internet or other sources, or may use the ones supplied on the CD (especially if time is limited). Using the storyboard as a guide, students will select appropriate layouts and backgrounds, then enter graphics and text onto the pre-formatted page. Finally, students will share their completed Mixbooks, either by embedding the animated book into an available website or by posting the link for others.

Software or Special Materials/Supplies:
Student Activity Sheet
Mixbook Storyboard
Flash-enabled web browser (Firefox recommended)
Resources for obtaining images (optional)

Standards:
NSES 5-8 Content Standard B
- An object that is not being subjected to a force will continue to move at a constant speed and in a straight line.
- If more than one force acts on an object along a straight line, then the forces will reinforce or cancel one another, depending on their direction and magnitude. Unbalanced forces will cause changes in the speed or direction of an object's motion.

Science TEKS

6.8e: The student knows force and motion are related to potential and kinetic energy. The student is expected to investigate how inclined planes and pulleys can be used to change the amount of force to move an object.

Procedures:
This lesson should follow an introduction to the simple machines and is intended for reinforcement.

Before Computer Work Begins

1. To introduce this activity, show the completed sample (SimpleMachinesSample.URL on CD).
2. Distribute the Student Activity Sheet and explain to students that they must explain and give common examples of each type of simple machine.
3. Distribute the blank Mixbook Storyboard sheets for students to plan their books. You may want to consider assigning both the Student Activity Sheet and Mixbook Storyboard for homework or completing them in class the day prior to creating the Mixbook.
4. Decide whether students will be responsible for obtaining their own images or will use the ones provided on the CD. If students are using the provided images, upload these files to a shared network location or distribute the files according to standard procedures.
5. Decide how the final Mixbooks will be shared and accessed. Students will either provide a link to the online book, or embed the book as a widget into another website (like a blog or wiki).
6. Print the necessary sections of the *User's Guide to Mixbook*.

Computer Activities

1. Remind students of the requirements for this project as stated on the Student Activity Sheet.
   - Title & Credits pages
   - 1-page spread for each simple machine type with the following text:
     - Name of machine
     - Characteristics/definition of the machine type
     - At least three common examples
   - At least three images representing each machine along with captions to explain how the machine works
2. Guide students in obtaining images, either from the ones supplied on the CD (which have been placed in a student-accessible location) or from various image websites (see the introductory section of this book for a list of some sites).
3. Guide students to http://www.mixbook.com.
4. If students have no Mixbook accounts, follow the account sign-up procedures outlined in the *User's Guide to Mixbook*.
5. Lead students in beginning a new project, referring to the User's Guide as needed.
6. Demonstrate how to upload the necessary images.
7. Walk students through the process of selecting and editing a background.
8. Using the storyboard as a guide, allow students time to add or remove pages as needed. Once the background is selected for either the cover or the first page, it may be best to duplicate that page rather than having to re-create the same background on each page.
9. Guide students in selecting appropriate layouts by practicing with page one.
10. Review, if necessary, how students can add photos or stickers to page one and make needed edits.
11. Demonstrate how to add and edit text elements on page one.
12. Make yourself available as students continue working at their own pace.
13. Lead students in publishing the book, including specific instructions on how to share their projects by linking or embedding.

Name: _____   Date: _____

Mixbook: Simple Machines

For this activity, you will create a Mixbook animated photo album with images and text to explain and give common examples of each type of simple machine. You must include the following in your Mixbook:
- Title & Credits pages
- 1-page spread for each simple machine type with the following text:
  - ○ Name of machine
  - ○ Characteristics/definition of the machine type
  - ○ At least three common examples
- At least three images representing each machine along with captions to explain how the machine works

Use this sheet as a guide to help plan for your project. In each box, fill in the appropriate information.

Machine:	Machine:
Definition: Common Examples:	Definition: Common Examples:
Machine:	Machine:
Definition: Common Examples:	Definition: Common Examples:
Machine:	Machine:
Definition: Common Examples:	Definition: Common Examples:

Student Activity

Mixbook: Common Uses of the Elements

Grade Level: Content Area(s):
Intermediate Science (5-8)

On CD-ROM:
ElementsSAS.pdf
ElementsSample.URL (shortcut to completed example – available only online)
Elements Images (folder)

Lesson Overview:
Students will use Mixbook to create an online animated book, using still images, titles, text, and stickers to illustrate and explain how elements from the periodic table are commonly used. Students may either gather images from the Internet or other sources, or may use the ones supplied on the CD (especially if time is limited). Using the storyboard as a guide, students will select appropriate layouts and backgrounds, then enter graphics and text onto the pre-formatted page. Finally, students will share their completed Mixbooks, either by embedding the animated book into an available website or by posting the link for others.

Software or Special Materials/Supplies:
Student Activity Sheet
Mixbook Storyboard
Flash-enabled web browser (Firefox recommended)
Resources for obtaining images (optional)

Standards:
NSES 5-8 Content Standard B
- A substance has characteristic properties, such as density, a boiling point, and solubility, all of which are independent of the amount of the sample. A mixture of substances often can be separated into the original substances using one or more of the characteristic properties.
- Chemical elements do not break down during normal laboratory reactions involving such treatments as heating, exposure to electric current, or reaction with acids. There are more than 100 known elements that combine in a multitude of ways to produce compounds, which account for the living and nonliving substances that we encounter.

Science TEKS

6.5a-b: The student knows the differences between elements and compounds. The student is expected to:
   a. know that an element is a pure substance represented by chemical symbols.
   b. recognize that a limited number of the many known elements comprise the largest portion of solid Earth, living matter, oceans, and the atmosphere.

Procedures:
This lesson can either follow a lesson on the periodic table, or be used for as an introductory lesson as long as students are given the proper resources for locating the information.

Before Computer Work Begins

1. To introduce this activity, show the completed sample (ElementsSample.URL on CD).
2. Distribute the Student Activity Sheet and explain to students that they must illustrate and explain the common uses of elements from the periodic table. Although the student activity sheet provides space for students to enter information about ten elements, you may want to assign fewer, depending upon the amount of available time.
3. Distribute the blank Mixbook Storyboard sheets for students to plan their books. You may want to consider assigning both the Student Activity Sheet and Mixbook Storyboard for homework or completing them in class the day prior to creating the Mixbook.
4. Decide whether students will be responsible for obtaining their own images or will use the ones provided on the CD. If students are using the provided images, upload these files to a shared network location or distribute the files according to standard procedures.
5. Decide how the final Mixbooks will be shared and accessed. Students will either provide a link to the online book, or embed the book as a widget into another website (like a blog or wiki).
6. Print the necessary sections of the *User's Guide to Mixbook*.

Computer Activities

1. Remind students of the requirements for this project as stated on the Student Activity Sheet.
   - Title & Credits pages
   - 1-page spread for each element with the following text:
     - Name of element
     - Symbol of the element
     - At least two examples of common uses of the element
   - At least three images representing each element's usage
2. Guide students in obtaining images, either from the ones supplied on the CD (which have been placed in a student-accessible location) or from various image websites (see the introductory section of this book for a list of some sites).
3. Guide students to http://www.mixbook.com.
4. If students have no Mixbook accounts, follow the account sign-up procedures outlined in the *User's Guide to Mixbook*.
5. Lead students in beginning a new project, referring to the User's Guide as needed.
6. Demonstrate how to upload the necessary images.
7. Walk students through the process of selecting and editing a background.
8. Using the storyboard as a guide, allow students time to add or remove pages as needed. Once the background is selected for either the cover or the first page, it may be best to duplicate that page rather than having to re-create the same background on each page.
9. Guide students in selecting appropriate layouts by practicing with page one.
10. Review, if necessary, how students can add photos or stickers to page one and make needed edits.
11. Demonstrate how to add and edit text elements on page one.
12. Make yourself available as students continue working at their own pace.
13. Lead students in publishing the book, including specific instructions on how to share their projects by linking or embedding.

Name: _____   Date: _____

Mixbook: Common Uses of Elements from the Periodic Table

For this activity, you will create a Mixbook animated photo album with images and text to describe how elements from the periodic table are commonly used. You must include the following in your Mixbook:
- Title & Credits pages
- 1-page spread for each element with the following text:
    - Name of element
    - Symbol of the element
    - At least two examples of common uses of the element
- At least three images representing each element's usage

Use this sheet as a guide to help plan for your project. In each box, fill in the appropriate information.

Element:

Common Examples:

Image Search Terms:

Element:

Common Examples:

Image Search Terms:

Element:

Common Examples:

Image Search Terms:

Element:

Common Examples:

Image Search Terms:

Element:

Common Examples:

Image Search Terms:

Element:

Common Examples:

Image Search Terms:

Element:

Common Examples:

Image Search Terms:

Element:

Common Examples:

Image Search Terms:

Element:

Common Examples:

Image Search Terms:

Element:

Common Examples:

Image Search Terms:

Student Activity
Wordle: 4 Seasons

Grade Level: Content Area(s):
Intermediate Science (5-8)

On CD-ROM:
4SeasonsSAS.pdf
FallSample.jpg
SpringSample.jpg
SummerSample.jpg
WinterSample.jpg

Lesson Overview:
Students will use Wordle to create a word cloud using words and phrases associated with the four seasons. Students will brainstorm ideas for each of the seasons and will use a Student Activity Sheet to record these ideas. Students will then create their Wordle and will refine the results until they are satisfied with the final result. Students will either print or create a screen capture of the Wordle.

Software or Special Materials/Supplies:
Student Activity Sheet
Flash-enabled web browser (Firefox recommended)

Standards:
NSES 5-8 Content Standard B
  • Seasons result from variations in the amount of the sun's energy hitting the surface, due to the tilt of the earth's rotation on its axis and the length of the day.

Science TEKS

4.8c: The student knows that there are recognizable patterns in the natural world and among the Sun, Earth, and Moon system. The student is expected to collect and analyze data to identify sequences and predict patterns of change in shadows, tides, seasons, and the observable appearance of the Moon over time.

8.7a: The student knows the effects resulting from cyclical movements of the Sun, Earth, and Moon. The student is expected to model and illustrate how the tilted Earth rotates on its axis, causing day and night, and revolves around the Sun causing changes in the seasons.

Procedures:
This lesson should follow a brief introduction of the four seasons and is intended to reinforce concepts that have already been introduced.

Before Computer Work Begins

1. Have students use the 4Seasons Student Activity Sheet to brainstorm words and phrases about the four seasons.
2. Print the necessary sections of the *User's Guide to Wordle*.

Computer Activities

1. Remind students of the requirements for this project as stated on the Student Activity Sheet.
2. Guide students to http://www.wordle.net/create.
3. Lead students in beginning a new project, referring to the User's Guide as needed.
4. Demonstrate how to insert the tilde (~) character between words in a phrase.
5. Demonstrate how to adjust size of words in the Wordle by increasing the number of times the word is entered into the list.
6. Students will click **GO** to create the Wordle, and then will revise the Wordle until a pleasing configuration is found.
7. Students will then print their Wordle, or will use a screen capture to save their Wordle as a .jpg or another format.

Name: _____ Date: _____

4 Seasons

Each of the 4 seasons is very different. List at least 5 words or phrases associated with each season. Complete the form below, and then create a Wordle for each season using those words. Remember when entering in phrases, they need a tilde (~) between each word to keep them together. For example, **warm weather** would need to be typed in as **warm~weather**. Type the title in several times so it is larger than the landforms.

www.wordle.net/create

Student Activity
Animoto Video: Water Cycle

Grade Level: Content Area(s):
Elementary/Intermediate Science (3-8)

On CD-ROM:
WaterCycleSAS.pdf
WaterCycleSample.mp4
Water Cycle Images (folder)
Water Cycle Title Slides (folder)

Lesson Overview:
Students will use Animoto to create a video using still images and title slides synchronized to a music track to illustrate the steps and sequence of the water cycle. Students may either gather images from the Internet or other sources, or may use the ones supplied on the CD (especially if time is limited). In addition, students will add titles to each stage of the cycle. These titles may be added from within Animoto or may be created using PowerPoint or other similar applications. The music soundtrack may be uploaded by students or may be chosen from Animoto's music library (recommended). Finally, students will share their completed videos, either by downloading the file, embedding the video into an available website, or posting the link for others.

Software or Special Materials/Supplies:
Student Activity Sheet
Animoto Storyboard
Flash-enabled web browser (Firefox recommended)
PowerPoint (optional)
Resources for obtaining images (optional)

Standards:
NSES 5-8 Content Standard D
  • Water, which covers the majority of the earth's surface, circulates through the crust, oceans, and atmosphere in what is known as the "water cycle." Water evaporates from the earth's surface, rises and cools as it moves to higher elevations, condenses as rain or snow, and falls to the surface where it collects in lakes, oceans, soil, and in rocks underground.
  • Water is a solvent. As it passes through the water cycle it dissolves minerals and gases and carries them to the oceans.
  • The sun is the major source of energy for phenomena on the earth's surface, such as growth of plants, winds, ocean currents, and the water cycle.

Science TEKS

3.8b: The student knows there are recognizable patterns in the natural world and among objects in the sky. The student is expected to describe and illustrate the Sun as a star composed of gases that provide light and heat energy for the water cycle.

4.5b: The student knows that matter has measurable physical properties and those properties determine how matter is classified, changed, and used. The student is expected to predict the changes caused by heating and cooling such as ice becoming liquid water and condensation forming on the outside of a glass of ice water.

5.8b: The student knows that there are recognizable patterns in the natural world and among the Sun, Earth, and Moon system. The student is expected to explain how the Sun and the ocean interact in the water cycle.

Procedures:

This lesson should follow a brief introduction of the water cycle and is intended for reinforcement.

Before Computer Work Begins

1. If you have not already done so, apply for an educator account at http://www.animoto.com to obtain the registration code for students. This must be done at least a week before the computer activity begins since the application approval process may take several days.
2. To introduce this activity, show the completed Water Cycle Animoto video. (WaterCycleSample.mp4)
3. Distribute the Student Activity Sheet and explain to students that they must explain and illustrate each step of the water cycle.
4. Distribute the blank Animoto Storyboard sheets for students to plan their videos. You may want to consider assigning both the Student Activity Sheet and Animoto Storyboard for homework or completing them in class the day prior to creating the Animoto video.
5. Decide whether students will be responsible for obtaining their own images or will use the ones provided on the CD. If students are using the provided images, upload these files to a shared network location or distribute the files according to standard procedures.
6. Decide whether students will be responsible for creating their own title/description slides or will use the ones provided on the CD. If students are using the provided text slides, upload these files to a shared network location or distribute the files according to standard procedures. Note that the PowerPoint file is included on the CD if you choose to alter the text before saving the slides as .jpg files.
7. Decide how the final Animoto videos will be shared and accessed. Students will either download and turn in the video file, provide a link to the online video, or embed the video into another website (like a blog or wiki).
8. Print the necessary sections of the *User's Guide to Animoto*.

Computer Activities

1. Remind students of the requirements for this project as stated on the Student Activity Sheet.
   - Title & Credits Slides
   - Title slide for each stage of the water cycle
   - Description slide of what happens at each stage in the water cycle
   - At least two images representing each stage of the cycle
2. Guide students in obtaining images, either from the ones supplied on the CD (which have been placed in a student-accessible location) or from various image websites (see the introductory section of this book for a list of some sites).
3. Direct students in creating their title/description slides. Limited title slides can be created within Animoto. However, description slides will need to be created using PowerPoint (or another application). Students may use the provided text slides (.jpg files) or edit the PowerPoint file to create their own.
4. Guide students to http://www.animoto.com.
5. If students have no Animoto accounts, follow the account sign-up procedures outlined in the *User's Guide to Animoto*.
6. Lead students in beginning a new full-length project, referring to the User's Guide as needed.
7. Demonstrate how to upload the necessary images, including any title/description slides (in .jpg format).
8. Allow students time to re-arrange and spotlight images according to their storyboards. If necessary, show students the process of adding title slides from within Animoto.
9. Guide students in selecting appropriate music.
10. Lead students in finalizing the video, including specific instructions on how to share their projects.

Name: _____   Date: _____

Animoto: Water Cycle Student Activity Sheet

For this activity, you will create a video using still images and text to show your understanding of the stages of the water cycle. You may choose to start at any step in the cycle. You must include the following in your Animoto video:

- Title & Credits Slides
- Title slide for each stage of the water cycle
- Description slide of what happens at each stage in the water cycle
- At least two images representing each stage of the cycle

Use this sheet as a guide to help plan for your project. In each box, fill in the appropriate information.

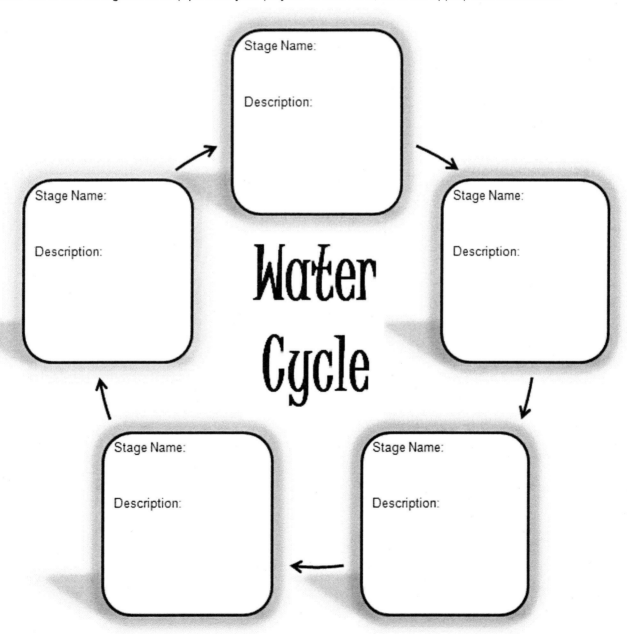

Student Activity
Animoto Video: Natural Disasters

Grade Level: Content Area(s):
Elementary/Intermediate Science (3-8)

On CD-ROM:
NaturalDisastersSAS.pdf
NaturalDisastersSample.mp4
Natural Disasters Images (folder)
Natural Disasters Title Slides (folder)

Lesson Overview:
Students will use Animoto to create a video using still images and title slides synchronized to a music track to illustrate and explain six natural disasters. Students may either gather images from the Internet or other sources, or may use the ones supplied on the CD (especially if time is limited). In addition, students will add titles to introduce and explain each of the natural disaster types. These titles may be added from within Animoto or may be created using PowerPoint or other similar applications. The music soundtrack may be uploaded by students or may be chosen from Animoto's music library (recommended). Finally, students will share their completed videos, either by downloading the file, embedding the video into an available website, or posting the link for others.

Software or Special Materials/Supplies:
Student Activity Sheet
Animoto Storyboard
Flash-enabled web browser (Firefox recommended)
PowerPoint (optional)
Resources for obtaining images (optional)

Standards:
NSES K-4 Content Standard D
- Weather changes from day to day and over the seasons.
- Objects in the sky have patterns of movement. The sun, for example, appears to move across the sky in the same way every day, but its path changes slowly over the seasons.

NSES 5-8 Content Standard D
- Seasons result from variations in the amount of the sun's energy hitting the surface, due to the tilt of the earth's rotation on its axis and the length of the day.

Science TEKS

3.7b: The student knows that Earth consists of natural resources and its surface is constantly changing. The student is expected to investigate rapid changes in Earth's surface such as volcanic eruptions, earthquakes, and landslides.

6.10c-d: The student understands the structure of the Earth, the rock cycle, and plate tectonics. The student is expected to:
   c. identify the major tectonic plates, including Eurasian, African, Indo-Australian, Pacific, North American, and South American.
   d. describe how plate tectonics causes major geological events such as ocean basins, earthquakes, volcanic eruptions, and mountain building.

8.10c: The student knows that climatic interactions exist among Earth, ocean, and weather systems. The student is expected to identify the role of the oceans in the formation of weather systems such as hurricanes.

Procedures:
This lesson should follow a brief introduction of natural disasters and is intended for reinforcement.

Before Computer Work Begins

1. If you have not already done so, apply for an educator account at http://www.animoto.com to obtain the registration code for students. This must be done at least a week before the computer activity begins since the application approval process may take several days.
2. To introduce this activity, show the completed Natural Disasters Animoto video. (NaturalDisastersSample.mp4)
3. Distribute the Student Activity Sheet and explain to students that they must illustrate and explain six natural disaster types in this project. Allow students plenty of time to complete the activity sheet.
4. Distribute the blank Animoto Storyboard sheets for students to plan their videos. You may want to consider assigning both the Student Activity Sheet and Animoto Storyboard for homework or completing them in class the day prior to creating the Animoto video.
5. Decide whether students will be responsible for obtaining their own images or will use the ones provided on the CD. If students are using the provided images, upload these files to a shared network location or distribute the files according to standard procedures.
6. Decide whether students will be responsible for creating their own title/description slides or will use the ones provided on the CD. If students are using the provided text slides, upload these files to a shared network location or distribute the files according to standard procedures. Note that the PowerPoint file is included on the CD if you choose to alter the text before saving the slides as .jpg files.
7. Decide how the final Animoto videos will be shared and accessed. Students will either download and turn in the video file, provide a link to the online video, or embed the video into another website (like a blog or wiki).
8. Print the necessary sections of the *User's Guide to Animoto*.

Computer Activities

1. Remind students of the requirements for this project as stated on the Student Activity Sheet.
   - Title & Credits Slides
   - Title slide for each type of natural disaster
   - Description or causes slide for each natural disaster
   - At least two images representing each natural disaster
2. Guide students in obtaining images, either from the ones supplied on the CD (which have been placed in a student-accessible location) or from various image websites (see the introductory section of this book for a list of some sites).
3. Direct students in creating their title/description slides. Limited title slides can be created within Animoto. However, description slides will need to be created using PowerPoint (or another application). Students may use the provided text slides (.jpg files) or edit the PowerPoint file to create their own.
4. Guide students to http://www.animoto.com.
5. If students have no Animoto accounts, follow the account sign-up procedures outlined in the *User's Guide to Animoto*.
6. Lead students in beginning a new full-length project, referring to the User's Guide as needed.
7. Demonstrate how to upload the necessary images, including any title/description slides (in .jpg format).
8. Allow students time to re-arrange and spotlight images according to their storyboards.
   If necessary, show students the process of adding title slides from within Animoto.
9. Guide students in selecting appropriate music.
10. Lead students in finalizing the video, including specific instructions on how to share their projects.

Name: _____   Date: ____ _____

Animoto: Natural Disasters Student Activity Sheet

For this activity, you will create a video using still images and text to show your understanding of the stages of six types of natural disasters. You must include the following in your Animoto video:

- Title & Credits Slides
- Title slide for each type of natural disaster
- Description or causes slide for each natural disaster
- At least two images representing each natural disaster

Use this sheet as a guide to help plan for your project. In each box, fill in the appropriate information.

Tornadoes	Description/Properties:

Hurricanes	Description/Properties:

Volcanoes	Description/Properties:

Tsunamis	Description/Properties:

Earthquakes	Description/Properties:

Wildfires	Description/Properties: